COHOMOLOGY THEORY

SZE-TSEN HU

Cohomology Theory

MARKHAM PUBLISHING COMPANY

Chicago

Dedicated to
MAXWELL HERMAN ALEXANDER NEWMAN

PREFACE

THE PRESENT BOOK is an introduction to cohomology theory. It is designed to supplement the author's "Homology Theory," published by Holden-Day in 1966, with fundamental materials enough for a one-year course in Algebraic Topology.

As in other books of the present author, leisurely detailed expositions will be given to a few carefully selected basic topics of the subject: namely, axiomatic characterization, singular theory, Alexander theory, products, and duality theorems. Intelligibility is always preferred to brevity, and unnecessary generalizations are avoided as much as possible.

The bibliography at the end of the book lists a number of related books on the subject, together with those books to which reference will be made in the text or in the exercises. Obviously, we have been most concerned with references to books for the convenience of the reader. References to the bibliography are letters, page numbers, and statement number, enclosed in brackets.

Cross references are given in the form (III. 5.7), where III stands for Chapter 3 and 5.7 for the numbering of the statement in the chapter. The chapter numeral will be omitted when the reference is made in the same chapter.

Certain deviations from standard set-theoretic notation have been adopted in the text: namely, $\Box$ is used to denote the empty set and $A \setminus B$ the set-theoretic difference usually denoted by $A - B$. We have used the symbol $\|$ to indicate the end of a proof and the abbreviation "iff" for the phrase "if and only if."

The author acknowledges with great pleasure the assistance he received in the form of financial support from the Air Force Office of Scientific Research and the National Science Foundation while the present book was being prepared. Finally, the author wishes to thank the publisher and the printer for their courtesy and cooperation.

Sze-Tsen Hu

University of California
Los Angeles, California

CONTENTS

Chapter 1

AXIOMATIC CHARACTERIZATION

IN THIS INITIAL CHAPTER of the book, we shall give the Eilenberg-Steenrod axioms of cohomology theory and deduce their consequences, including the cellular cohomology theory. Proofs are mostly omitted since they are dual to those in homology theory given in [H5].

1. Eilenberg-Steenrod Axioms

First of all, let us recall the notion of an admissible category for homology and cohomology theories as defined in [H5, pp. 1–5].

By an *admissible category for homology and cohomology theories*, we mean a category $\mathscr{C}$, in the sense of [H2, p. 192], whose objects are certain topological pairs — that is, pairs of the form (X, A), where X is a topological space and A is a subspace of X [H1, p. 16] — and whose morphisms are certain (continuous) maps of topological pairs satisfying the five conditions (AC1) through (AC5), listed as follows:

(AC1)   If a topological pair (X, A) is an object in $\mathscr{C}$, then $\mathscr{C}$ contains all topological pairs and inclusion maps in the *lattice* of (X, A) shown by the following diagram:

$$(\square, \square) \rightarrow (A, \square) \quad \begin{array}{c} (X, \square) \\ \nearrow \qquad \searrow \\ \\ \searrow \qquad \nearrow \\ (A, A) \end{array} \quad (X, A) \rightarrow (X, X)$$

(AC2)   If a map $f: (X, A) \rightarrow (Y, B)$ is a morphism in $\mathscr{C}$, then $\mathscr{C}$ contains the topological pairs (X, A) and (Y, B) together with all maps

1

that f defines from members of the lattice of (X, A) into corresponding members of the lattice of (Y, B).

(AC3) If the maps $f\colon (X, A) \to (Y, B)$ and $g\colon (Y, B) \to (Z, C)$ are morphisms in $\mathscr{C}$, then $\mathscr{C}$ contains their composition $g \circ f\colon (X, A) \to (Z, C)$.

(AC4) If a topological pair (X, A) is an object in $\mathscr{C}$, then $\mathscr{C}$ contains the *cylinder* $(X, A) \times I$ defined by

$$(X, A) \times I = (X \times I, A \times I) \qquad I = [0, 1],$$

and the two *canonical imbeddings* κ_0, κ_1 of (X, A) into $(X, A) \times I$ defined by

$$\kappa_0(x) = (x, 0), \qquad \kappa_1(x) = (x, 1)$$

for every $x \in X$.

(AC5) There is a singleton space P_0 in $\mathscr{C}$. If P is any singleton space in $\mathscr{C}$, then $\mathscr{C}$ contains every map $f\colon P \to X$ into any space X in $\mathscr{C}$.

In (AC5), we have identified the topological pair $(X, \square)$ with the topological space X itself. This traditional identification will be used throughout the book.

In particular, the category $\mathscr{C}_T$ of all topological pairs and all maps of such pairs obviously satisfies the five conditions (AC1) through (AC5) and hence is an admissible category. Clearly, $\mathscr{C}_T$ is the largest admissible category; that is, $\mathscr{C}_T$ contains every admissible category as a subcategory. For other examples of admissible categories, see [H5, p. 4].

Throughout the remainder of the present section, let $\mathscr{C}$ denote any given admissible category for homology and cohomology theories. By (AC5), $\mathscr{C}$ contains a singleton space P_0 which will be referred to as the *distinguished singleton space* in $\mathscr{C}$.

By a *cohomology theory* on the category $\mathscr{C}$, we mean a collection

$$\mathscr{H} = \{H, *, \delta\}$$

of three functions as follows:

The first function H assigns to each topological pair (X, A) in $\mathscr{C}$ and each integer q (positive, negative, or zero) an Abelian group

$$H^q(X, A)$$

which will be called the *q-dimensional cohomology group of the topological pair (X, A) in the cohomology theory $\mathscr{H}$*. In the literature, $H^q(X, A)$ is frequently called the *q-dimensional (relative) cohomology group of the topological space X modulo its subspace A*. In the case $A = \square$, it is called the *q-dimensional (absolute) cohomology group of the space X*.

The second function $*$ assigns to each map $f: (X, A) \to (Y, B)$ in $\mathscr{C}$ and each integer q a homomorphism

$$f^* = f^{*q}: H^q(Y, B) \to H^q(X, A)$$

which will be called the *homomorphism induced by the map f in the co-homology theory* $\mathscr{H}$.

The third function δ assigns to each topological pair (X, A) in $\mathscr{C}$ and each integer q a homomorphism

$$\delta = \delta(X, A, q): H^{q-1}(A) \to H^q(X, A)$$

which will be referred to as the *coboundary operator*.

Furthermore, these three functions H, $*$, and δ are required to satisfy the following seven conditions (I–VII), called *the Eilenberg-Steenrod axioms for cohomology theory*:

Axiom I (*Identity Axiom*). *If $i: (X, A) \to (X, A)$ is the identity map on a topological pair (X, A) in $\mathscr{C}$, then the induced homomorphism*

$$i^*: H^q(X, A) \to H^q(X, A)$$

is the identity automorphism of the group $H^q(X, A)$ for every integer q.

Axiom II (*Composition Axiom*). *If $f: (X, A) \to (Y, B)$ and $g: (Y, B) \to (Z, C)$ are maps in $\mathscr{C}$, then we have*

$$(g \circ f)^{*q} = f^{*q} \circ g^{*q}$$

for every integer q.

Hence, for every fixed integer q, the function H^q and $*^q$ constitute a *contravariant functor* from the category $\mathscr{C}$ to the category $\mathscr{A}$ of all Abelian groups and all homomorphisms of such groups [H2, p. 195]. If we introduce the notation

$$H^q(f) = f^{*q}$$

for every map f in $\mathscr{C}$, this contravariant functor may be denoted by H^q and will be called the *q-dimensional cohomology functor in the cohomology theory* $\mathscr{H}$.

Axiom III (*Commutativity Axiom*). *If $f: (X, A) \to (Y, B)$ is a map in $\mathscr{C}$ and if $g: A \to B$ is the map in $\mathscr{C}$ defined by $g(x) = f(x)$ for every $x \in A$, then*

$$\delta \circ g^* = f^* \circ \delta$$

holds in the following diagram:

$$
\begin{array}{ccc}
H^{q-1}(B) & \xrightarrow{\ \ g^*\ \ } & H^{q-1}(A) \\
\downarrow{\scriptstyle \delta} & & \downarrow{\scriptstyle \delta} \\
H^q(Y, B) & \xrightarrow{\ \ f^*\ \ } & H^q(X, A)
\end{array}
$$

for every integer q.

　　This axiom ties up the cohomology functors H^q in the cohomology theory $\mathscr{H}$ by means of the coboundary operator δ.

　　The first three axioms (I–III) are usually called the *algebraic axioms.*

　　Axiom IV (*Exactness Axioms*).　*If (X, A) is a topological pair in $\mathscr{C}$ and if*

$$
i: A \to X, \qquad j: X \to (X, A)
$$

denote the inclusion maps, then the infinite sequence

$$
\cdots \to H^{q-1}(A) \xrightarrow{\ \ \delta\ \ } H^q(X, A) \xrightarrow{\ \ j^*\ \ } H^q(X) \xrightarrow{\ \ i^*\ \ } H^q(A) \to \cdots
$$

of groups and homomorphisms, called the cohomology sequence of (X, A), is exact in the sense that at every group of the sequence the image of the input homomorphism is identical with the kernel of the output homomorphism.

　　Axiom V (*Homotopy Axiom*).　*If two maps $f, g: (X, A) \to (Y, B)$ in $\mathscr{C}$ are homotopic in $\mathscr{C}$, that is, if there exists a map*

$$
h: (X, A) \times I \to (Y, B)
$$

in $\mathscr{C}$ satisfying $f = h \circ \kappa_0$ and $g = h \circ \kappa_1$, where κ_0 and κ_1 denote the two canonical imbeddings of (X, A) into $(X, A) \times I$, then we have

$$
f^{*q} = g^{*q}
$$

for every integer q.

　　Axiom VI (*Excision Axiom*).　*If U is an open set of a topological space X whose closure $\mathrm{Cl}(U)$ is contained in the interior of a subspace A of X and if the inclusion map*

$$
e: (X \backslash U, A \backslash U) \to (X, A)
$$

is in $\mathscr{C}$, then the induced homomorphism

$$
e^{*q}: H^q(X, A) \to H^q(X \backslash U, A \backslash U)
$$

is an isomorphism for every integer q.

The inclusion map e is called the *excision* of the open set U and e^{*q} is called its *q-dimensional excision isomorphism*.

Axiom VII (*Dimension Axiom*). *The q-dimensional cohomology group $H^q(P_0)$ of the distinguished singleton space P_0 consists of a single element for every integer $q \neq 0$; or, in symbols,*

$$H^q(P_0) = 0 \qquad (q \neq 0).$$

This completes the definition of a *cohomology theory* $\mathscr{H}$ on the given admissible category $\mathscr{C}$. If $\mathscr{H}$ satisfies only the first six axioms, then $\mathscr{H}$ is known as a *generalized cohomology theory* on the admissible category $\mathscr{C}$.

The zero-dimensional cohomology group

$$G = H^0(P_0)$$

of the distinguished singleton space P_0 in $\mathscr{C}$ is called the *coefficient group* of the cohomology theory $\mathscr{H}$. Thus, the dimension axiom locates the coefficient group at the right dimension.

The consistency of the axioms is shown by the *trivial cohomology theory* $\mathscr{H}_0$ on the admissible category $\mathscr{C}$ defined by setting

$$H^q(X, A) = 0$$

for every topological pair (X, A) in $\mathscr{C}$ and every integer q. This also proves the existence of a cohomology theory with trivial coefficient group $G = 0$ on any given admissible category $\mathscr{C}$. Of course, the interest lies in the existence of nontrivial cohomology theories. The existence of such on any given admissible category $\mathscr{C}$ and with any prescribed coefficient group G can be established by either the *singular theory* or the *Alexander theory*, constructed in the next two chapters with arbitrarily given coefficient group G and on the largest admissible category $\mathscr{C}_T$ and, hence, also on any given admissible category $\mathscr{C}$.

Thus, we have seen that cohomology theory is parallel (or *dual*) to homology theory studied in [H5]. In fact, they differ essentially in only one point: namely, homology functors are covariant while cohomology functors are contravariant. Because of this duality, one can expect a dual theorem in cohomology theory for every theorem established in homology theory.

For the convenience of those readers who use this text as a reference book, the remainder of the present chapter is devoted to the consequences of the axioms dual to those established in [H5, Chaps. I–V]. It is recommended that readers who have worked out these dualizations given in [H5] as exercises skip the rest of the chapter.

EXERCISES

1A. Prove that the homotopy axiom (V) for cohomology theory is equivalent to these statements: *If (X, A) is a topological pair in $\mathscr{C}$, then the two canonical imbeddings $\kappa_0, \kappa_1 : (X, A) \to (X, A) \times I$ induce the same homomorphism; in symbols, $\kappa_0^* = \kappa_1^*$.*

1B. Prove that the excision axiom (VI) for cohomology theory is equivalent to these statements: *If X_1 and X_2 are two subspaces of a topological space X such that X_1 is closed and*

$$X = \text{Int}(X_1) \cup \text{Int}(X_2)$$

and if the inclusion map

$$i : (X_1, X_1 \cap X_2) \to (X, X_2)$$

is in $\mathscr{C}$, then the induced homomorphism

$$i^* : H^q(X, X_2) \to H^q(X_1, X_1 \cap X_2)$$

is an isomorphism for every integer q.

1C. By means of axioms I, II, and VII, prove that, for every singleton space X in $\mathscr{C}$, we have

$$H^q(X) \approx \begin{cases} 0 & (\text{if } q \neq 0), \\ G & (\text{if } q = 0), \end{cases}$$

where G denotes the coefficient group of the cohomology theory.

1D. For each topological pair (X, A) in the admissible category $\mathscr{C}$, the direct sum

$$H^*(X, A) = \Sigma_q H^q(X, A)$$

is called the *total cohomology group* of the pair (X, A) in the cohomology theory $\mathscr{H}$. Show that the induced homomorphisms i^*, j^* and the coboundary operator δ in the cohomology sequence of the pair (X, A) determine homomorphisms in the following triangle:

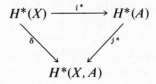

Prove the exactness of this triangle; that is, at every corner the image of the input homomorphism coincides with the kernel of the output homomorphism.

2. Immediate Consequences

Throughout the present section, let

$$\mathscr{H} = \{H, *, \delta\}$$

denote any cohomology theory on an arbitrarily given admissible category $\mathscr{C}$.

To establish the *homotopy invariance* of the cohomology groups in $\mathscr{H}$, let us first define homotopy equivalences in the category $\mathscr{C}$.

A map $f: (X, A) \to (Y, B)$ in $\mathscr{C}$ is said to be a *homotopy equivalence in* $\mathscr{C}$ iff there exists a map $g: (Y, B) \to (X, A)$ in $\mathscr{C}$ such that the composed maps $g \circ f$ and $f \circ g$ are homotopic in $\mathscr{C}$ to the identity maps on (X, A) and (Y, B), respectively. In case $\mathscr{C} = \mathscr{C}_T$, $A = \square$, and $B = \square$, this notion of homotopy equivalence reduces to the one defined in [H1, p. 51].

If a homotopy equivalence $f: (X, A) \to (Y, B)$ in $\mathscr{C}$ exists, then we say that the topological pair (X, A) is *homotopically equivalent in* $\mathscr{C}$ to the topological pair (Y, B); in symbols,

$$(X, A) \simeq_{\mathscr{C}} (Y, B).$$

In the case $\mathscr{C} = \mathscr{C}_T$, $A = \square$, and $B = \square$, this reduces to the notation

$$X \simeq Y$$

defined in [H1, p. 52].

Proposition 2.1. *If a map $f: (X, A) \to (Y, B)$ in $\mathscr{C}$ is a homotopy equivalence in $\mathscr{C}$, then the induced homomorphism*

$$f^*: H^q(Y, B) \to H^q(X, A)$$

is an isomorphism for every integer q.

The proof of (2.1) is dual to that of [H5, p. 14, (3.1)] and hence is omitted.

In the case $A = \square$ and $B = \square$, we have the following corollary of (2.1).

Corollary 2.2. *If two topological spaces X and Y in $\mathscr{C}$ are homotopically equivalent in $\mathscr{C}$, that is, $X \simeq_{\mathscr{C}} Y$, then we have*

$$H^q(X) \approx H^q(Y)$$

for every integer q.

A topological space X in $\mathscr{C}$ is said to be *contractible in* $\mathscr{C}$ iff the identity map $i: X \to X$ is homotopic in $\mathscr{C}$ to a constant map in $\mathscr{C}$. In case $\mathscr{C} = \mathscr{C}_T$, it reduces to the notion of contractibility defined in [H1, p. 50]. Since a topological space X in $\mathscr{C}$ which is contractible in $\mathscr{C}$ is obviously homotopically equivalent in $\mathscr{C}$ to the distinguished singleton space P_0, we have the following corollary of (2.2) and the dimension axiom (VII).

Corollary 2.3. *If a topological space X in $\mathscr{C}$ is contractible in $\mathscr{C}$, then we have*

$$H^q(X) \approx \begin{cases} G & (\text{if } q = 0), \\ 0 & (\text{if } q \neq 0), \end{cases}$$

where G denotes the coefficient group of the cohomology theory $\mathscr{H}$.
Next let us deduce some consequences of the exactness axiom.

Proposition 2.4. *If the inclusion map $i: A \rightarrow X$ of a subspace A of a topological space X is in $\mathscr{C}$ and is a homotopy equivalence in $\mathscr{C}$, then we have*

$$H^q(X, A) = 0$$

for every integer g.
The proof of (2.4) is dual to that of [H5, p. 15, (3.4)] and hence is omitted.
Applying (2.4) to the case $A = X$, we obtain the following corollary.

Corollary 2.5. *For every topological space X in $\mathscr{C}$, we have*

$$H^q(X, X) = 0$$

for every integer q.
Next let us establish an improvement of the excision axiom.

Proposition 2.6. *If U is an open set of a topological space X contained in a subspace A of X and if the inclusion map*

$$e: (X \backslash U, A \backslash U) \rightarrow (X, A)$$

is in $\mathscr{C}$, then e induces an isomorphism

$$e^*: H^q(X, A) \approx H^q(X \backslash U, A \backslash U)$$

for every integer q provided that there exists an open set V of the space X such that the closure $\mathrm{Cl}(V)$ is contained in U and the inclusion map

$$h: (X \backslash U, A \backslash U) \rightarrow (X \backslash V, A \backslash V)$$

is a homotopy equivalence in $\mathscr{C}$.
The proof of (2.6) is dual to that of [H5, p. 19, 3.10] and hence is omitted.

Next let us consider an arbitrary map

$$f: (X, A) \to (Y, B)$$

in the category $\mathscr{C}$. Let $g: X \to Y$ and $h: A \to B$ denote the maps defined by f. Then we obtain the following diagram of groups and homomorphisms:

$$\cdots \to H^{q-1}(B) \xrightarrow{\delta} H^q(Y, B) \xrightarrow{j^*} H^q(Y) \xrightarrow{i^*} H^q(B) \to \cdots$$
$$\downarrow h^* \qquad\quad \downarrow f^* \qquad\quad \downarrow g^* \qquad\quad \downarrow h^*$$
$$\cdots \to H^{q-1}(A) \xrightarrow{\delta} H^q(X, A) \xrightarrow{j^*} H^q(X) \xrightarrow{i^*} H^q(A) \to \cdots$$

called the *cohomology ladder* of the map f in the cohomology theory $\mathscr{H}$. Here, the two horizontal rows are the cohomology sequences of the pairs (X, A) and (Y, B). According to the exactness axiom, these are exact. On the other hand, it follows from axioms II and III that the squares are commutative; that is, we have

$$\delta \circ h^* = f^* \circ \delta, \quad j^* \circ f^* = g^* \circ j^*, \quad i^* \circ g^* = h^* \circ i^*.$$

Furthermore, it is easy to verify that δ sends $\mathrm{Im}(h^*)$ into $\mathrm{Im}(f^*)$, j^* sends $\mathrm{Im}(f^*)$ into $\mathrm{Im}(g^*)$, and i^* sends $\mathrm{Im}(g^*)$ into $\mathrm{Im}(h^*)$. For every integer q, denote

$$K^q(X, A) = \mathrm{Coker}\,(f^*), \quad K^q(X) = \mathrm{Coker}\,(g^*), \quad K^q(A) = \mathrm{Coker}\,(h^*).$$

Then the homomorphisms i^*, j^*, δ in the cohomology sequence of the pair (X, A) induce homomorphisms

$$i^*: \quad K^q(X) \to K^q(A),$$
$$j^*: \quad K^q(X, A) \to K^q(X),$$
$$\delta: \quad K^{q-1}(A) \to K^q(X, A)$$

for every integer q. Therefore, we obtain an infinite sequence

$$\cdots \to K^{q-1}(A) \xrightarrow{\delta} K^q(X, A) \xrightarrow{j} K^q(X) \xrightarrow{i} K^q(A) \xrightarrow{\delta} K^{q+1}(X, A) \to \cdots$$

which will be referred to as the *cokernel sequence* of the map f: $(X, A) \to (Y, B)$. Clearly this sequence is *semiexact* in the sense of [H2, p. 96].

Now let us apply this to the case $(Y, B) = (P_0, P_0)$, where P_0 denotes the distinguished singleton space in $\mathscr{C}$. Assume that, for every topological pair (X, A) in $\mathscr{C}$, the constant map

$$\theta: \quad (X, A) \to (P_0, P_0)$$

is in $\mathscr{C}$.

The cokernel sequence of this map θ is called the *reduced cohomology sequence* of the topological pair (X, A) in the cohomology theory $\mathscr{H}$ and will be denoted by

$$\cdots \to \tilde{H}^{q-1}(A) \xrightarrow{\delta} \tilde{H}^q(X, A) \xrightarrow{j^*} \tilde{H}^q(X) \xrightarrow{i^*} \tilde{H}^q(A) \to \cdots.$$

Since the groups in the cohomology sequence of the pair (P_0, P_0) are trivial except for the two zero-dimensional cohomology groups $H^0(P_0) = G$, we have

$$\tilde{H}^q(X, A) = H^q(X, A) \qquad \text{(all } q),$$

$$\tilde{H}^q(X) = H^q(X), \qquad \tilde{H}^q(A) = H^q(A) \qquad (q \neq 0).$$

The two new groups $\tilde{H}^0(X)$ and $\tilde{H}^0(A)$ in the reduced cohomology sequence of (X, A) are called the *reduced zero-dimensional cohomology groups* of the spaces X and A. For the sake of convenience, all groups $\tilde{H}^q(A)$, $\tilde{H}^q(X)$, and $\tilde{H}^q(X, A)$ in the reduced cohomology sequence of (X, A) will be called *reduced cohomology groups*.

Proposition 2.7. *For an arbitrary nonempty topological space X in $\mathscr{C}$, we have*

$$H^0(X) \approx G \oplus \tilde{H}^0(X).$$

The proof of (2.7) is dual to that of [H5, p. 23, (4.2)] and hence is omitted.

Proposition 2.8. *If a nonempty topological space X in $\mathscr{C}$ is contractible in $\mathscr{C}$, then we have*

$$\tilde{H}^q(X) \approx 0$$

for every integer q.

The proof of (2.8) is dual to that of [H5, p. 26, (4.9)] and hence is omitted.

Now let us consider an arbitrary map

$$f \colon X \to Y$$

in $\mathscr{C}$ and assume that the constant maps $\sigma \colon X \to P_0$ and $\rho \colon Y \to P_0$ are in $\mathscr{C}$. Since $\sigma = \rho \circ f$, the following triangle is commutative:

$$H^0(Y) \xrightarrow{f^*} H^0(X)$$

$$\rho^* \nwarrow \qquad \nearrow \sigma^*$$

$$H^0(P_0)$$

It follows that f^* sends $\text{Im}(\rho^*)$ into $\text{Im}(\sigma^*)$ and hence induces a homomorphism

$$f^*: \tilde{H}^0(Y) \to \tilde{H}^0(X)$$

which will be called the *induced homomorphism of the map f: $X \to Y$ on the reduced cohomology group*. In particular, the homorphism

$$i^*: \quad \tilde{H}^0(X) \to \tilde{H}^0(A)$$

in the reduced cohomology sequence of (X,A) is the induced homomorphism of the inclusion map i: $A \to X$.

Since $\tilde{H}^q(X) = H^q(X)$ holds for every $q \neq 0$, we have induced homomorphisms

$$f^*: \quad \tilde{H}^q(Y) \to \tilde{H}^q(X)$$

of the reduced cohomology groups for all integers q. As immediate consequences of axioms I, II, and V, we have the following propositions.

Proposition 2.9. *If i: $X \to X$ is the identity map on a topological space X in $\mathscr{C}$, then the induced homorphism*

$$i^*: \quad \tilde{H}^q(X) \to \tilde{H}^q(X)$$

is the identity automorphism of the group $\tilde{H}^q(X)$ for every integer q.

Proposition 2.10. *If $f: X \to Y$ and $g: Y \to Z$ are maps in $\mathscr{C}$, then we have*

$$(g \circ f)^* = f^* \circ g^*: \tilde{H}^q(Z) \to \tilde{H}^q(X)$$

for every integer q.

Proposition 2.11. *If two maps $f,g: X \to Y$ in $\mathscr{C}$ are homotopic in $\mathscr{C}$, then we have*

$$f^* = g^*: \tilde{H}^q(Y) \to \tilde{H}^q(X)$$

for every integer q.

As an immediate consequence of these three propositions, we have the following corollary.

Corollary 2.12. *If two topological spaces X and Y in $\mathscr{C}$ are homotopically equivalent in $\mathscr{C}$, then we have*

$$\tilde{H}^q(X) \approx \tilde{H}^q(Y)$$

for every integer q.

By dualizing the proof of [H5, p. 25, (4.8)], one can establish the following important theorem.

Theorem 2.13. *For any topological pair (X, A) in $\mathscr{C}$ with $X \neq \square$ and $A \neq \square$, the reduced cohomology sequence*

$$\cdots \to \tilde{H}^{q-1}(A) \xrightarrow{\ \delta\ } \tilde{H}^q(X, A) \xrightarrow{\ j^*\ } \tilde{H}^q(X) \xrightarrow{\ i^*\ } \tilde{H}^q(A) \to \cdots$$

of (X, A) is exact.

Now let us study the suspensions. Let X be any nonempty topological space and let I denote the closed unit interval $[0, 1]$ of real numbers. If in the topological product $X \times I$ we identify the sets $X \times 0$ and $X \times 1$ with single points u and v, respectively, we obtain a quotient space $S(X)$, which is called the *suspension* of the topological space X. Let

$$p : X \times I \to S(X)$$

denote the natural projection. Then X can be considered as a subspace of $S(X)$ by means of an imbedding

$$i : X \to S(X)$$

defined by $i(x) = p(x, \tfrac{1}{2})$ for every $x \in X$.

Let U and V denote the subspaces of $S(X)$ defined by

$$U = \{p(x, t) | x \in X \text{ and } 0 \leqslant t \leqslant \tfrac{1}{2}\},$$

$$V = \{p(x, t) | x \in X \text{ and } \tfrac{1}{2} \leqslant t \leqslant 1\}.$$

Then, U and V are clearly both contractible. Furthermore, we have

$$U \cap V = X, \qquad U \cup V = S(X).$$

To establish an isomorphism between the reduced cohomology groups $\tilde{H}^q(X)$ and $\tilde{H}^{q+1}[S(X)]$, let us assume that $\mathscr{C}$ contains all pairs and maps to be used below. Since V is contractible, it follows from (2.8) and (2.13) that

$$\delta : \tilde{H}^q(X) \to H^{q+1}(V, X)$$

is an isomorphism for every integer q. On the other hand, since U is contractible, it follows from (2.8) and (2.13) that

$$j^* : H^{q+1}[S(X), U] \to \tilde{H}^{q+1}[S(X)]$$

is an isomorphism for every integer q. Finally, it follows from (2.6) that the inclusion map

$$e : (V, X) \to [S(X), U]$$

induces an isomorphism

$$e^*: H^{q+1}[S(X), U] \to H^{q+1}(V, X)$$

for every integer q. The composed isomorphism

$$\sigma = j^* \circ e^{*-1} \circ \delta: \tilde{H}^q(X) \approx \tilde{H}^{q+1}[S(X)]$$

will be called the *suspension isomorphism* on the group $\tilde{H}^q(X)$ in the cohomology theory $\mathscr{H}$.

As an application of the suspension isomorphisms, we can determine the cohomology groups of the *n*-sphere S^n.

Proposition 2.14. *For each integer $n \geq 0$, the reduced cohomology group of the n-sphere S^n is as follows:*

$$\tilde{H}^q(S^n) \approx \begin{cases} G & (\text{if } q = n), \\ 0 & (\text{if } q \neq n), \end{cases}$$

where G denotes the coefficient group of the cohomology theory $\mathscr{H}$.

The proof of (2.14) is essentially the same as that of [H5, p. 28, (5.1)] and hence is omitted.

As an immediate consequence of (2.7) and (2.14), we obtain the co-homology groups of S^n as stated in the following corollary.

Corollary 2.15. *The cohomology groups of the n-sphere S^n are as follows:*

$$H^q(S^n) \approx \begin{cases} 0 & (\textit{if } n \neq q \neq 0), \\ G & (\textit{if } n \neq q = 0 \text{ or } n = q \neq 0), \\ G \oplus G & (\textit{if } n = q = 0), \end{cases}$$

where G denotes the coefficient group of the cohomology theory $\mathscr{H}$.

Now let us consider an arbitrary map $f: X \to Y$ in $\mathscr{C}$. Define a map

$$S(f): S(X) \to S(Y)$$

by setting

$$S(f)[p(x, t)] = p[f(x), t]$$

for every $x \in X$ and every $t \in I$. This map $S(f)$ is called the *suspension* of f. Assume that $S(f)$ is in $\mathscr{C}$.

Proposition 2.16.   *The commutativity relation* $\sigma \circ f^* = [S(f)]^* \circ \sigma$ *holds in the following rectangle:*

$$
\begin{array}{ccc}
\tilde{H}^q(Y) & \xrightarrow{\ \sigma\ } & \tilde{H}^{q+1}[S(Y)] \\
\downarrow{\scriptstyle f^*} & & \downarrow{\scriptstyle [S(f)]^*} \\
\tilde{H}^q(X) & \xrightarrow{\ \sigma\ } & \tilde{H}^{q+1}[S(X)]
\end{array}
$$

where σ *stands for the suspension isomorphisms.*

The proof of (2.16) is dual to that of [H5, p. 30, (5.3)] and hence is omitted.

By a *topological triple* (X, A, B), we mean a topological space X together with two subspaces A and B of X satisfying $B \subset A$. Consider an arbitrarily given topological triple (X, A, B) such that the inclusion maps

$$\bar{i}: (A, B) \to (X, B), \qquad \bar{j}: (X, B) \to (X, A)$$

are in $\mathscr{C}$.

For every integer q, the composition

$$\bar{\delta} = \delta \circ k^*: H^{q-1}(A, B) \to H^q(X, A)$$

of the homomorphisms

$$H^{q-1}(A, B) \xrightarrow{\ k^*\ } H^{q-1}(A) \xrightarrow{\ \delta\ } H^q(X, A),$$

where k^* is induced by the inclusion map $k: A \to (A, B)$ and δ is the coboundary operator of the pair (X, A), will be referred to as the *coboundary operator* of the topological triple (X, A, B) in the cohomology theory $\mathscr{H}$. Together with the induced homomorphisms of the maps $\bar{i}$ and $\bar{j}$, these coboundary operators give rise to an infinite sequence

$$\cdots \to H^{q-1}(A, B) \xrightarrow{\ \bar{\delta}\ } H^q(X, A) \xrightarrow{\ \bar{j}^*\ } H^q(X, B) \xrightarrow{\ \bar{i}^*\ } H^q(A, B) \to \cdots$$

of Abelian groups and homomorphisms which will be called the *cohomology sequence* of the topological triple (X, A, B) in the cohomology theory $\mathscr{H}$.

Theorem 2.17.   *The cohomology sequence of a topological triple* (X, A, B) *in the cohomology theory* $\mathscr{H}$ *is exact.*

The proof of (2.17) is dual to that of [H5, p. 32, (6.1)] and hence is omitted.

Consider any two topological triples (X, A, B) and (Y, C, D). By a *map*

$$f: (X, A, B) \to (Y, C, D)$$

from (X, A, B) *into* (Y, C, D), we understand that f is a map from X into Y satisfying $f(A) \subset C$ and $f(B) \subset D$. If this is the case, then f defines the following three maps of topological pairs:

$$g: (X, A) \to (Y, C), \quad h: (X, B) \to (Y, D), \quad k: (A, B) \to (C, D).$$

Then we obtain the following diagrams of groups and homomorphisms:

$$\cdots \to H^{q-1}(C, D) \xrightarrow{\bar{\delta}} H^q(Y, C) \xrightarrow{\bar{j}^*} H^q(Y, D) \xrightarrow{\bar{i}^*} H^q(C, D) \to \cdots$$

$$\Big\downarrow k^* \qquad\qquad \Big\downarrow g^* \qquad\qquad \Big\downarrow h^* \qquad\qquad \Big\downarrow k^*$$

$$\cdots \to H^{q-1}(A, B) \xrightarrow{\bar{\delta}} H^q(X, A) \xrightarrow{\bar{j}^*} H^q(X, B) \xrightarrow{\bar{i}^*} H^q(A, B) \to \cdots$$

called the *cohomology ladder* of the map f in the cohomology theory $\mathscr{H}$. Here, the two horizontal rows are the cohomology sequences of the topological triples (X, A, B) and (Y, C, D). According to (2.17), these are exact. On the other hand, one can easily verify by means of axioms II and III that the rectangles are commutative.

By a *separation* $X_1 | X_2$ of a given topological space X, we mean two nonempty open subspaces X_1 and X_2 of X satisfying

$$X_1 \cup X_2 = X, \qquad X_1 \cap X_2 = \square.$$

Consequently, X_1 and X_2 are also closed subspaces of X. A topological space X is said to be *separated* in case a separation $X_1 | X_2$ of X has been given.

Now let us consider an arbitrary topological pair (X, A) in $\mathscr{C}$, where the space X is separated with a given separation $X_1 | X_2$. Let

$$A_1 = A \cap X_1, \qquad A_2 = A \cap X_2.$$

Assume that the inclusion maps

$$i_1: (X_1, A_1) \to (X, A), \qquad i_2: (X_2, A_2) \to (X, A)$$

are in $\mathscr{C}$.

Theorem 2.18. *For every integer q, the induced homomorphisms*

$$i_1^*: H^q(X, A) \to H^q(X_1, A_1)$$
$$i_2^*: H^q(X, A) \to H^q(X_2, A_2)$$

are epimorphisms, and the homomorphism

$$\phi = i_1^* \oplus i_2^*: H^q(X, A) \to H^q(X_1, A_1) \oplus H^q(X_2, A_2)$$

defined by $\phi(x) = [i_1^*(x), i_2^*(x)]$ *for every element* x *of* $H^q(X, A)$ *is an isomorphism.*

The proof of (2.18) is dual to that of [H5, p. 41, (7.2)] and hence is omitted.

EXERCISES

2A. Let $f: X \to Y$ denote a map in $\mathscr{C}$ which is homotopic in $\mathscr{C}$ to a constant map. Prove that the induced homomorphism

$$f^*: H^q(Y) \to H^q(X)$$

in the given cohomology theory $\mathscr{H}$ is trivial; that is, $f^* = 0$ for every integer $q \neq 0$.

2B. Consider any map $f: (X, A) \to (Y, B)$ in the category $\mathscr{C}$ and let $g: X \to Y$ and $h: A \to B$ denote the maps defined by f. Prove the following assertions:

   (a) If g^* and h^* are isomorphisms for every integer q, so is f^*.
   (b) If h^* and f^* are isomorphisms for every integer q, so is g^*.
   (c) If f^* and g^* are isomorphisms for every integer q, so is h^*.

2C. Assume that $\mathscr{C} = \mathscr{C}_T$ and prove the following assertions:

   (a) The q-dimensional cohomology group $H^q(X)$ in $\mathscr{H}$ of a topological space X is a *homotopy property* of X as defined in [H1, p. 53].
   (b) If a subspace A of a topological space X is a *retract* of X as defined in [H1, p. 32], then the inclusion map $i: A \to X$ induces epimorphisms, the inclusion map $j: X \to (X, A)$ induces monomorphisms, and the coboundary operators of the pair (X, A) are trivial homomorphisms. Furthermore, for each integer q, $H^q(X)$ is isomorphic to the direct sum of $H^q(A)$ and $H^q(X, A)$.
   (c) If a topological space X is *deformable* into a subspace A of X as defined in [H5, p. 17], then the inclusion map $i: A \to X$ induces monomorphisms, the inclusion map $j: X \to (X, A)$ induces trivial homomorphisms, and the coboundary operators of the pair (X, A) are epimorphisms. Furthermore, for each integer q, $H^q(A)$ is isomorphic to the direct sum of $H^q(X)$ and $H^{q+1}(X, A)$.
   (d) If a map $f: (X, A) \to (Y, B)$ is *deformable* into the subspace B of Y as defined in [H5, p. 20], then the induced homomorphism

$$f^*: H^q(Y, B) \to H^q(X, A)$$

   is trivial for every integer q.
   (e) Generalize parts (a) through (d) to the case where $\mathscr{C}$ is an arbitrary admissible category.

3. Uniqueness Theorem

Throughout the present section, let $\mathscr{C}$ denote a given admissible category which contains the category $\mathscr{C}_{FP}$ of all *cellular pairs* and all maps of such pairs as defined in [H5, p. 4]. For the definition of *cellular polytopes*, see [H1, pp. 128–129].

First, let us consider an arbitrarily given cohomology theory

$$\mathscr{H} = \{H, *, \delta\}$$

on the admissible category $\mathscr{C}$.

For each integer $n \geqslant 0$, let Δ^n denote *unit n-simplex*, which is defined as the subspace of the $(n + 1)$-dimensional Euclidean space R^{n+1} consisting of all points $(x_0, x_1, \ldots, x_n)$ of R^{n+1} such that $x_i \geqslant 0$ for every $i = 0, 1, \ldots, n$ and that

$$x_0 + x_1 + \cdots + x_n = 1.$$

By the *boundary* $\partial\Delta^n$ of Δ^n, we mean the subspace

$$\partial\Delta^n = \{(x_0, x_1, \ldots, x_n) \in \Delta^n | x_0 x_1 \cdots x_n = 0\}$$

of Δ^n which is homeomorphic to the unit $(n-1)$-sphere S^{n-1} in the Euclidean space R^n. In case $n = 0$, Δ^0 consists of a single point, namely, the real number 1 of the real line R, and $\partial\Delta^0$ is empty.

Proposition 3.1. *For every nonnegative integer n, we have*

$$H^q(\Delta^n, \partial\Delta^n) \approx \begin{cases} G & (\text{if } q = 0), \\ 0 & (\text{if } q \neq n), \end{cases}$$

where G denotes the coefficient group of the cohomology theory $\mathscr{H}$.

The proof of (3.1) is dual to that of [H5, p. 45, (8.1)] and hence is omitted.

Next let us consider any finite cellular pair (X, A); that is to say, X is a finite cellular polytope, and A is a subpolytope of X.

Let $n \geqslant 0$ denote a given integer and assume that the residual space $X \backslash A$ consists of the interior of $m > 0$ n-dimensional cells $\xi_1, \xi_2, \ldots, \xi_m$ of X. In symbols, we have

$$X \backslash A = \text{Int}(\xi_1) \cup \text{Int}(\xi_2) \cup \cdots \cup \text{Int}(\xi_m).$$

Let $M = \{1, 2, \ldots, m\}$ and, for each $i \in M$, let

$$\phi_i: \partial\Delta^n \to A$$

denote the *characteristic map* of the n-cell ξ of X as defined in [H1,

p. 128]. Give M the discrete topology and consider the topological products

$$D = M \times \Delta^n, \qquad B = M \times \partial\Delta^n.$$

Then B is a subpolytope of the finite cellular polytope D. Define a map

$$f: B \to A$$

by taking $f(i, t) = \phi_i(t)$ for every $i \in M$ and every $t \in \partial\Delta^n$. According to the definition of cellular polytopes in [H1, p. 128], X is the *adjunction space* obtained by adjoining D to A by means of the map f as defined in [H1, p. 122].

Thus, X is a quotient space of the disjoint topological sum

$$W = D + A$$

as defined in [H1, p. 36]. Let us consider the natural projection

$$p: W \to X$$

from W onto its quotient space X. For each integer $i \in M$, define a map

$$p_i: (\Delta^n, \partial\Delta^n) \to (X, A)$$

by taking $p_i(t) = p(i, t)$ for every $t \in \Delta^n$. Then we have

$$\phi_i = p_i|\partial\Delta^n$$

and p_i sends $\Delta^n \backslash \partial\Delta^n$ homeomorphically onto $\text{Int}(\xi_i)$.

Proposition 3.2.   *For every integer q, the induced homomorphisms*

$$p_i^*: H^q(X, A) \to H^q(\Delta^n, \partial\Delta^n) \qquad (i = 1, 2, \ldots, m)$$

are epimorphisms, and the homomorphism

$$h: H^q(X, A) \to H^q(\Delta^n, \partial\Delta^n) \oplus \cdots \oplus H^q(\Delta^n, \partial\Delta^n)$$

from $H^q(X, A)$ to the direct sum of m copies of the group $H^q(\Delta^n, \partial\Delta^n)$ defined by

$$h(x) = [p_1^*(x), \ldots, p_m^*(x)]$$

for every element x of $H^q(X, A)$ is an isomorphism.

The proof of (3.2) is dual to that of [H5, p. 46, (8.2)] and hence is omitted.

The following corollary is a direct consequence of (3.1) and (3.2).

Corollary 3.3. *If (X, A) is a finite cellular pair such that $X \setminus A$ consists of the interior of m n-dimensional cells of X, then we have*

$$H^q(X, A) = 0 \qquad (q \neq n),$$

and $H^n(X, A)$ is isomorphic to the direct sum $G \oplus \cdots \oplus G$ of m copies of the coefficient group G in the cohomology theory $\mathscr{H}$.

By the *n-dimensional skeleton* of a cellular polytope X, we mean its subpolytope X_n, which consists of all cells of X of dimension $\leqslant n$ [H1, p. 129]. Thus, we have $X_{-1} = \square$.

Let (X, A) denote any finite cellular pair. We define its *relative dimension* $\dim(X, A)$ as follows: In the case $X \setminus A = \square$, we set $\dim(X, A) = -1$; otherwise, $\dim(X, A)$ is the smallest integer n satisfying

$$X \setminus A \subset X_n.$$

Proposition 3.4. *If (X, A) is a finite cellular pair of relative dimension n, then we have*

$$H^q(X, A) = 0$$

for every $q < 0$ and every $q > n$.

The proof of (3.4) is dual to that of [H5, p. 49, (8.4)] and hence is omitted.

By induction on the integer $\dim(X \setminus A) - n$, one can easily establish the following proposition.

Proposition 3.5. *For an arbitrary finite cellular pair (X, A), the induced homomorphism*

$$i_n^*: H^q(X, A) \to H^q(X_n \cup A, A)$$

of the inclusion map $i_n: (X_n \cup A, A) \to (X, A)$, where X_n denotes the n-dimensional skeleton of X, is an isomorphism for every $q < n$ and is a monomorphism for $q = n$.

By means of (3.5) and some suitable excisions, one can easily establish the following proposition.

Proposition 3.6. *For an arbitrary finite cellular pair (X, A), the induced homomorphism*

$$j_n^*: H^q(X, A) \to H^q(X_n, A_n)$$

of the inclusion map $j_n: (X_n, A_n) \to (X, A)$, where X_n and A_n stand for the *n-dimensional skeletons of X and A, is an isomorphism for every $q < n$ and is a monomorphism for $q = n$.*

To state the *uniqueness theorem*, let

$$\mathscr{H} = \{H, *, \delta\}, \qquad \mathscr{H}' = \{H', \#, \delta'\}$$

denote arbitrary cohomology theories defined on admissible categories $\mathscr{C}$ and $\mathscr{C}'$ each containing the category $\mathscr{C}_{FP}$ of all finite cellular pairs and all maps of such pairs. Let

$$G = H^0(P_0), \qquad G' = H'^0(P_0)$$

denote the coefficient groups, where $P_0 \in \mathscr{C}_{FP}$ is a common distinguished singleton space for both $\mathscr{H}$ and $\mathscr{H}'$.

Theorem 3.7. *Let $h\colon G \to G'$ denote an arbitrarily given homomorphism. Then, for every finite cellular pair (X, A) and every integer q, there exists a unique homomorphism*

$$h_q\colon H^q(X, A) \to H'^q(X, A)$$

satisfying the following three conditions:

(1) $h_0 = h$ on $G = H^0(P_0)$.

(2) *For every map $f\colon (X, A) \to (Y, B)$ in $\mathscr{C}_{FP}$ and every integer q, the commutativity relation*

$$h_q \circ f^* = f \circ h_q$$

holds in the following rectangle:

$$
\begin{array}{ccc}
H^q(Y, B) & \xrightarrow{\;f^*\;} & H^q(X, A) \\
\downarrow{\scriptstyle h_q} & & \downarrow{\scriptstyle h_q} \\
H'^q(Y, B) & \xrightarrow{\;f^{\#}\;} & H'^q(X, A)
\end{array}
$$

(3) *For every finite cellular pair (X, A) and every integer q, the commutativity relation*

$$h_q \circ \delta = \delta' \circ h_{q-1}$$

holds in the following rectangle:

$$
\begin{array}{ccc}
H^{q-1}(A) & \xrightarrow{\;\delta\;} & H^q(X, A) \\
\downarrow{\scriptstyle h_{q-1}} & & \downarrow{\scriptstyle h_q} \\
H'^{q-1}(A) & \xrightarrow{\;\delta'\;} & H'^q(X, A)
\end{array}
$$

The proof of (3.7) is dual to that of [H5, p. 51, (9.1)] and hence is omitted.

Corollary 3.8 (*Uniqueness Theorem*).   *If h*: $G \to G'$ *is an isomorphism, then so is*

$$h_q: H^q(X, A) \to H'^q(X, A)$$

for every finite cellular pair (X, A) *and every integer q.   Hence, for any given coefficient group G, there is essentially only one cohomology theory on the category* $\mathscr{C}_{FP}$.

The proof of (38.) is the same as that of [H5, p. 52, (9.2)] and hence is omitted.

EXERCISES

3A. Let (X, A) denote a finite cellular pair satisfying $X_n \subset A$. By either (3.5) or (3.6), prove that $H^q(X, A) = 0$ holds for every $q \leqslant n$.

3B. Consider the homomorphism h_q in (3.7).   Prove that, for every finite cellular polytope X, the homomorphism

$$h_q: H^q(X) \to H'^q(X)$$

induces a homomorphism

$$\tilde{h}_q: \tilde{H}^q(X) \to \tilde{H}'^q(X)$$

of the reduced cohomology groups.   Prove the following assertions:

(a) If h is an isomorphism, then so is h_q for every finite cellular polytope X and every integer q.

(b) For every map $f: X \to Y$ from a finite cellular polytope X into a finite cellular polytope Y and every integer q, the following rectangle is commutative:

$$
\begin{array}{ccc}
\tilde{H}^q(Y) & \xrightarrow{\;f^*\;} & \tilde{H}^q(X) \\
\downarrow{\scriptstyle \tilde{h}_q} & & \downarrow{\scriptstyle \tilde{h}_q} \\
\tilde{H}'^q(Y) & \xrightarrow{\;f^\#\;} & \tilde{H}'^q(X)
\end{array}
$$

(c) For every finite cellular polytope X and every integer q, the following rectangle is commutative:

$$
\begin{array}{ccc}
\tilde{H}^q(X) & \xrightarrow{\;\sigma\;} & \tilde{H}^{q+1}[S(X)] \\
\downarrow{\scriptstyle \tilde{h}_q} & & \downarrow{\scriptstyle \tilde{h}_{q+1}} \\
\tilde{H}'^q(X) & \xrightarrow{\;\sigma'\;} & \tilde{H}'^{q+1}[S(X)]
\end{array}
$$

where σ and σ' denote the suspension isomorphisms in the cohomology theories $\mathcal{H}$ and $\mathcal{H}'$, respectively.

4. Further Consequences

Throughout the present section, let $\mathcal{H}$ denote a given cohomology theory of the largest admissible category $\mathcal{C}_T$ of all topological pairs and all maps of such pairs with an arbitrary coefficient group G, unless otherwise stated. Properties of $\mathcal{H}$ were studied in the preceding section as far as necessary for the proof of the uniqueness theorem. The present section is devoted to deriving further consequences of the axioms of the cohomology theory $\mathcal{H}$. Every result established for $\mathcal{H}$ can be easily generalized to cohomology theories on the arbitrary admissible category $\mathcal{C}$ by adding suitable conditions so that topological pairs, maps, and homotopies involved in the proof as well as the statement of the result are in $\mathcal{C}$.

First let us consider an arbitrarily given map

$$f: X \to Y$$

in the category $\mathcal{C}_T$. Let

$$Z = Z(f)$$

denote the *mapping cylinder* of the given map f as defined in [H1, p. 45] or in [H5, p. 63]. Then X and Y can be considered as subspaces of Z. Let

$$g: Y \to (Z, X)$$

denote the inclusion map. Then we obtain an infinite sequence

$$\cdots \to H^{q-1}(X) \xrightarrow{\delta} H^q(Z, X) \xrightarrow{g^*} H^q(Y) \xrightarrow{f^*} H^q(X) \to \cdots$$

of Abelian groups and homomorphisms, where δ stands for the coboundary operators in $\mathcal{H}$ for the pair (Z, X). This infinite sequence will be called the *cohomology sequence* of the map f in $\mathcal{H}$.

Proposition 4.1. *The cohomology sequence of any map $f: X \to Y$ in the cohomology theory $\mathcal{H}$ is exact.*

The proof of (4.1) is dual to that of [H5, p. 66, (1.6)] and hence is omitted.

Obviously, a similar result holds for the reduced cohomology groups. In fact, we have the following proposition.

Proposition 4.2. *The reduced cohomology sequence*

$$\cdots \to \tilde{H}^{q-1}(X) \xrightarrow{\delta} H^q(Z, X) \xrightarrow{g^*} \tilde{H}^q(Y) \xrightarrow{f^*} \tilde{H}^q(X) \to \cdots$$

of any map $f: X \to Y$ is exact.

Assume $X \neq \square$. If we identify the subspace X of the mapping cylinder $Z(f)$ of the given map $f: X \to Y$ to a single point u, we obtain a quotient space $C(f)$ which is called the *mapping cone* of f. Then Y can be considered as a subspace of $C(f)$. Let

$$P(f): Y \to C(f)$$

denote the inclusion map which will be referred to as the *associated imbedding* of the given map f.

Proposition 4.3. *For an arbitrary map $f: X \to Y$ in $\mathscr{C}_T$ with $X \neq \square$ and every integer q, the sequence*

$$\tilde{H}^q[C(f)] \xrightarrow{[P(f)]^*} \tilde{H}^q(Y) \xrightarrow{f^*} \tilde{H}^q(X)$$

is exact; in other words, the kernel of f^* coincides with the image of $[P(f)]^*$.

The proof of (4.3) is dual to that of [H5, p. 69, (2.3)] and hence is omitted.

Next let us identify the subspace Y of the mapping cone $C(f)$ of the given map $f: X \to Y$ to a single point v. Then we obtain the suspension $S(X)$ of X as the quotient space. Let

$$Q(f): C(f) \to S(X)$$

denote the natural projection. Besides, let us also consider the suspension

$$S(f): S(X) \to S(Y)$$

of the given map $f: X \to Y$.

Proposition 4.4 *For an arbitrary map $f: X \to Y$ in $\mathscr{C}_T$ with $X \neq \square$ and every integer q, the sequence*

$$\tilde{H}^q[S(Y)] \xrightarrow{[S(f)]^*} \tilde{H}^q[S(X)] \xrightarrow{[Q(f)]^*} \tilde{H}^q[C(f)] \xrightarrow{[P(f)]^*} \tilde{H}^q(Y) \xrightarrow{f^*} \tilde{H}^q(X)$$

of induced homomorphisms is exact.

The proof of (4.4) is dual to that of [H5, p. 72, (3.1)] and hence is omitted.

For each integer q, let

$$\tau = [Q(f)]^* \circ \sigma: \tilde{H}^{q-1}(X) \to \tilde{H}^q[C(f)]$$

where $\sigma: \tilde{H}^{q-1}(X) \to \tilde{H}^q[S(X)]$ denotes the suspension isomorphism. Then the following corollary is an immediate consequence of (4.4).

Corollary 4.5. *The following infinite sequence*

$$\cdots \to \tilde{H}^{q-1}(X) \xrightarrow{\tau} \tilde{H}^q[C(f)] \xrightarrow{[P(f)]^*} \tilde{H}^q(Y) \xrightarrow{f^*} \tilde{H}^q(X) \to \cdots$$

is exact and will be referred to as Puppe's cohomology sequence of the map f in the cohomology theory $\mathcal{H}$.

The excision axiom of the cohomology theory $\mathcal{H}$ asserts that the inclusion map

$$e: (X \backslash U, A \backslash U) \to (X, A),$$

where U stands for an open set of X, induces isomorphisms on cohomology groups in the theory $\mathcal{H}$ if the condition

$$\mathrm{Cl}(U) \subset \mathrm{Int}(A)$$

is satisfied. On many occasions, only the weaker condition

$$U \subset A$$

is available. Under this relaxed condition, the conclusion is not always true. However, we have the following theorem.

Theorem 4.6. *For every integer q, the induced homomorphism*

$$e^*: H^q(X, A) \to H^q(X \backslash U, A \backslash U)$$

of the inclusion map $e: (X \backslash U, A \backslash U) \to (X, A)$, where $U \subset A$ is an open set of X, is an isomorphism provided that at least one of the following two conditions is satisfied:

(a)   *There exists an open set V of X such that the closure $\mathrm{Cl}(V)$ is contained in U and the inclusion map*

$$h: (X \backslash U, A \backslash U) \to (X \backslash V, A \backslash V)$$

is a homotopy equivalence.

(b)   *There exists a subspace B of X such that $A \subset V$, $\text{Cl}(U) \subset \text{Int}(B)$, and the inclusions maps*

$$i: A \to B, \qquad j: A \backslash U \to B \backslash U$$

are homotopy equivalences.

The proof of (4.6) is dual to that of [H5, p. 76, (4.1)] and hence is omitted.

As an application of (4.6), one can establish the following excision theorem for finite cellular pairs.

Theorem 4.7. *If (X, A) is a finite cellular pair and if U is an open set of X such that U is contained in A and that $A \backslash U$ is a subpolytope of A, then*

$$e^*: H^q(X, A) \to H^q(X \backslash U, A \backslash U)$$

of the inclusion map $e: (X \backslash U, A \backslash U) \to (X, A)$ is an isomorphism for every integer q.

The proof of (4.7) is dual to that of [H5, p. 77, (4.2)] and hence is omitted.

Applying (4.7) to the special case $U = \text{Int}(A)$, we obtain the following corollary.

Corollary 4.8. *For any finite cellular pair (X, A), the induced homomorphism*

$$e^*: H^q(X, A) \to H^q[X \backslash \text{Int}(A), \partial A]$$

of the inclusion map $e: [X \backslash \text{Int}(A), \partial A] \to (X, A)$ is an isomorphism for every integer q.

As another form of (4.8), we give the following corollary.

Corollary 4.9. *If A and B are two subpolytopes of a finite cellular polytope X satisfying*

$$X = A \cup B,$$

then the induced homomorphisms

$$d^*: H^q(X, B) \to H^q(A, A \cap B),$$
$$e^*: H^q(X, A) \to H^q(B, A \cap B)$$

of the inclusion maps $d: (A, A \cap B) \to (X, B)$ and $e: (B, A \cap B) \to (X, A)$ are isomorphisms for every integer q.

By a *topological triad* $(X; A, B)$, we mean a topological space X together with an ordered pair (A, B) of subspaces A and B of X. The topological triad $(X; A, B)$ is said to be *proper* (with respect to the cohomology theory $\mathcal{H}$) iff the inclusion maps

$$\alpha: (A, A \cap B) \to (A \cup B, B),$$
$$\beta: (B, A \cap B) \to (A \cup B, A)$$

induce isomorphisms

$$\alpha^*: H^q(A \cup B, B) \to H^q(A, A \cap B),$$
$$\beta^*: H^q(A \cup B, A) \to H^q(B, A \cap B)$$

in the cohomology theory $\mathcal{H}$ for every integer q. For examples of proper topological triads, see [H5, p. 89].

Theorem 4.10. *A topological triad* $(X; A, B)$ *is proper iff, for every integer* q, *the inclusion maps*

$$i: (A, A \cap B) \to (A \cup B, A \cap B),$$
$$j: (B, A \cap B) \to (A \cup B, A \cap B)$$

induce epimorphisms

$$i^*: H^q(A \cup B, A \cap B) \to H^q(A, A \cap B),$$
$$j^*: H^q(A \cup B, A \cap B) \to H^q(B, A \cap B)$$

and the homomorphism

$$\phi = i^* \oplus j^*: H^q(A \cup B, A \cap B) \to H^q(A, A \cap B) \oplus H^q(B, A \cap B),$$

defined by $\phi(\xi) = [i^*(\xi), j^*(\xi)]$ *for every element* ξ *of* $H^q(A \cup B, A \cap B)$, *is an isomorphism.*

The proof of (4.10) is dual to that of [H5, p. 89, (6.2)] and hence is omitted.

Now let $(X; A, B)$ denote an arbitrarily given proper topological triad. Consider the homomorphisms

$$H^{q-1}(A, A \cap B) \xleftarrow{\alpha^*} H^{q-1}(A \cup B, B) \xrightarrow{l^*} H^{q-1}(A \cup B) \xrightarrow{\delta} H^q(X, A \cup B)$$

for any integer q, where δ is the coboundary operator for the pair $(X, A \cup B)$ and α^*, l^* are induced homomorphisms of the inclusion maps. Since α^* is an isomorphism, we may define a homomorphism

$$\delta^*: H^{q-1}(A, A \cap B) \to H^q(X, A \cup B)$$

for every integer q by taking

$$\delta^* = \delta \circ l^* \circ \alpha^{*-1}.$$

This homomorphism δ^* will be referred to as the *coboundary operator* for the proper triad $(X; A, B)$.

Thus we obtain an infinite sequence

$$\cdots \to H^{q-1}(A, A \cap B) \xrightarrow{\delta^*} H^q(X, A \cup B) \xrightarrow{k^*} H^q(X, B) \xrightarrow{h^*} H^q(A, A \cap B) \to \cdots$$

of homomorphisms, where h^* and k^* are the induced homomorphisms of the inclusion maps. This infinite sequence is called the *cohomology sequence* of the proper triad $(X; A, B)$ in the cohomology theory $\mathscr{H}$.

Theorem 4.11. *The cohomology sequence of any proper topological triad $(X; A, B)$ is exact.*

The proof of (4.11) is dual to that of [H5, p. 91, (63)] and hence is omitted.

Now let $(X; A, B)$ denote a proper topological triad satisfying

$$A \cup B = X, \qquad A \cap B = C.$$

Theorem 4.12. *If $h, h_1, h_2: (X, C) \to (Y, D)$ are maps from the topological pair (X, C) into a topological pair (Y, D) satisfying*

$$\begin{aligned}
h_1 \mid A = h \mid A, &\qquad h_1(B) \subset D, \\
h_2 \mid B = h \mid B, &\qquad h_2(A) \subset D,
\end{aligned}$$

then the induced homomorphisms

$$h^*, h_1^*, h_2^*: H^q(Y, D) \to H^q(X, C)$$

satisfy the relation

$$h^* = h_1^* + h_2^*$$

for every integer q.

The proof of (4.12) is dual to that of [H5, p. 94, (7.1)].

If the subspace D of the space Y is homologically trivial, for example, if D is contractible, then (4.12) implies a similar theorem for the reduced cohomology groups of X and Y.

Theorem 4.13.   *Let $h,h_1,h_2: (X, C) \to (Y, D)$ denote maps from the topological pair (X, C) into a topological pair (Y, D) satisfying*

$$h_1 \mid A = h \mid A, \qquad h_1(B) \subset D,$$
$$h_2 \mid B = h \mid B, \qquad h_2(A) \subset D.$$

If the subspace D of the space Y is contractible and the maps

$$f,f_1,f_2: X \to Y$$

are defined by the maps h, h_1, h_2, respectively, then the induced homomorphisms

$$f^*,f_1^*,f_2^*: \tilde{H}^q(Y) \to \tilde{H}^q(X)$$

satisfy the relation

$$f^* = f_1^* + f_2^*$$

for every integer q.

Finally, let us construct the *Mayer-Vietoris cohomology sequence* of an arbitrarily given proper topological triad $(X; A, B)$ satisfying

$$X = A \cup B, \qquad C = A \cap B.$$

For this purpose, let us first define for every integer q a homomorphism

$$\phi: H^q(X) \to H^q(A) \oplus H^q(B)$$

from $H^q(X)$ into the direct sum $H^q(A) \oplus H^q(B)$ by taking

$$\phi(u) = [m_1^*(u), m_2^*(u)]$$

for every element u of $H^q(X)$, where

$$m_1^*: H^q(X) \to H^q(A), \qquad m_2^*: H^q(X) \to H^q(B)$$

are the induced homomorphisms of the inclusion maps $m_1: A \to X$ and $m_2: B \to X$.

Next, for every integer q, define a homomorphism

$$\psi: H^q(A) \oplus H^q(B) \to H^q(C)$$

from the direct sum $H^q(A) \oplus H^q(B)$ into $H^q(C)$ by taking

$$\psi(\xi, \eta) = h_1^*(\xi) - h_2^*(\eta)$$

for every element (ξ, η) of $H^q(A) \oplus H^q(B)$, where

$$h_1^*: H^q(A) \to H^q(C), \qquad h_2^*: H^q(B) \to H^q(C)$$

are the induced homomorphisms of the inclusion maps $h_1: C \to A$ and $h_2: C \to B$.

Finally, for every integer q, consider the following hexagon of homomorphisms:

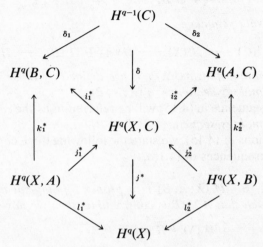

Here δ, δ_1, δ_2 are coboundary operators while the remaining homomorphisms are induced by inclusion maps. The triangles are commutative, k_1^* and k_2^* are isomorphisms, and

$$\text{Im}(j_1^*) = \text{Ker}(i_2^*), \qquad \text{Im}(j_2^*) = \text{Ker}(i_1^*), \qquad j^* \circ \delta = 0.$$

Therefore, it follows from the *hexagonal lemma* in [H5, pp. 106–107, (9.1)–(9.2)] that we may define a homomorphism

$$\Delta: H^{q-1}(C) \to H^q(X)$$

by taking

$$\Delta = -l_1^* \circ k_1^{*-1} \circ \delta_1 = l_2^* \circ k_2^{*-1} \circ \delta_2.$$

Thus we obtain an infinite sequence

$$\cdots \to H^{q-1}(C) \xrightarrow{\Delta} H^q(X) \xrightarrow{\phi} H^q(A) \oplus H^q(B) \xrightarrow{\psi} H^q(C) \to \cdots$$

called the *Mayer-Vietoris cohomology sequence* of the proper topological triad $(X; A, B)$.

Theorem 4.14. *The Mayer-Vietoris cohomology sequence of any proper topological triad $(X; A, B)$ with $X = A \cup B$ is exact.*

The proof of (4.14) is dual to that of [H5, p. 108, (9.3)] and hence is omitted.

Instead of the usual cohomology sequences, we may use the reduced cohomology sequences provided that $C \neq \square$. Hence we obtain the following proposition.

Proposition 4.15.   *For any proper topological triad* $(X; A, B)$ *with*

$$X = A \cup B, \qquad C = A \cap B \neq \square,$$

we have an exact sequence

$$\cdots \to \tilde{H}^{q-1}(C) \xrightarrow{\Delta} \tilde{H}^q(X) \xrightarrow{\phi} \tilde{H}^q(A) \oplus \tilde{H}^q(B) \xrightarrow{\psi} \tilde{H}^q(C) \to \cdots,$$

where the homomorphisms Δ, ϕ, ψ *are defined by those of the Mayer-Vietoris cohomology sequence of* $(X; A, B)$.

The exact sequence in (4.15) will be referred to as the *reduced Mayer-Vietoris cohomology sequence* of $(X; A, B)$.

As applications of (4.15), we state the following three corollaries which are direct consequences of (4.15).

Corollary 4.16.   *If* $(X; A, B)$ *is a proper topological triad with* $X = A \cup B$ *and such that* $A \cap B$ *is contractible, then we have*

$$\tilde{H}^q(X) \approx \tilde{H}^q(A) \oplus \tilde{H}^q(B)$$

for every integer q.

Corollary 4.17.   *If* $(X; A, B)$ *is a proper topological triad with*

$$X = A \cup B, \qquad C = A \cap B \neq \square,$$

and such that X *is contractible, then we have*

$$\tilde{H}^q(C) \approx \tilde{H}^q(A) \oplus \tilde{H}^q(B)$$

for every integer q.

Corollary 4.18.   *If* $(X; A, B)$ *is a proper topological triad with*

$$X = A \cup B, \qquad C = A \cap B \neq \square,$$

and such that A, B *are contractible, then the homomorphism*

$$\Delta \colon \tilde{H}^{q-1}(C) \to \tilde{H}^q(X)$$

is an isomorphism for every integer q.

EXERCISES
4A. Prove that, for any *relative n-cell* (X, A) as defined in [H5, p. 74], the induced homomorphism

$$i^* \colon \tilde{H}^q(X) \to \tilde{H}^q(A)$$

of the inclusion map $i: A \to X$ is an epimorphism if $q = n$; a monomorphism if $q = n - 1$; and an isomorphism if $q \neq n$ and $q \neq n - 1$.

4B. Let $f: (X, A) \to (Y, B)$ denote a *relative homeomorphism* of regular compact Hausdorff pairs as defined in [H5, pp. 82–84]. Prove that the induced homomorphism

$$f^*: H^q(Y, B) \to H^q(X, A)$$

is an isomorphism for every integer q.

4C. Consider any two proper topological triads $(X; A, B)$ and $(Y; C, D)$. Let

$$f: (X; A, B) \to (Y; C, D)$$

denote a map from the space X into the space Y satisfying

$$f(A) \subset C, \qquad f(B) \subset D.$$

Construct the *cohomology ladder* of the map f and prove the commutativity of its rectangles.

4D. Prove that the induced homomorphism

$$f^*: H^n(S^n) \to H^n(S^n)$$

of any map $f: S^n \to S^n$ of degree k is given by

$$f^*(x) = kx$$

for every element x of $H^n(S^n)$.

4E. Dualize the computations given in [H5, Chap. III] to calculate the cohomology groups of graphs, surfaces, real projective spaces, complex projective spaces, lens spaces, etc.

4F. Let $(X; A, B)$ denote any proper topological triad. Analogous to the Mayer-Vietoris cohomology sequence in the text, define an infinite sequence

$$\cdots \to H^{q-1}(X, A \cap B) \xrightarrow{\Delta} H^q(X, A \cup B) \xrightarrow{\phi} H^q(X, A) \otimes H^q(X, B) \xrightarrow{\psi} H^q(X, A \cap B) \to \cdots$$

This sequence is called the *relative Mayer-Vietoris cohomology sequence* of the triad $(X; A, B)$. Prove the exactness of this sequence.

5. Cellular Cohomology Groups

Let G denote an arbitrary Abelian group. Consider any given finite cellular pair (X, A). We recall that the free Abelian group

$$\mathbf{C}_n(X, A)$$

generated by the set $S_n(X, A)$ of all (open) n-cells in $X \setminus A$ is called the *n-dimensional integral chain group* of the cellular pair (X, A).

For every integer n, consider the Abelian group

$$\mathbf{C}^n(X, A; G) = \text{Hom } [\mathbf{C}_n(X, A), G]$$

of all homomorphisms from $\mathbf{C}_n(X, A)$ into G as defined in [H2, p. 109]. This Abelian group $\mathbf{C}^n(X, A; G)$ will be called the *group of n-dimensional cochains of (X, A) over G.*

Using the boundary operator

$$\partial\colon \mathbf{C}_{n+1}(X, A) \rightarrow \mathbf{C}_n(X, A)$$

of integral chains defined in [H5, p. 191], we define a homomorphism

$$\delta\colon \mathbf{C}^n(X, A; G) \rightarrow \mathbf{C}^{n+1}(X, A; G)$$

by taking

$$\delta = \text{Hom}(\partial, i)$$

as defined in [H2, p. 110], where $i\colon G \rightarrow G$ denotes the identity homomorphism. This homomorphism δ will be called the *coboundary operator* on the group $\mathbf{C}^n(X, A; G)$.

Lemma 5.1. *The composition $\delta \circ \delta$ of the homomorphisms*

$$\mathbf{C}^{n-1}(X, A; G) \xrightarrow{\delta} \mathbf{C}^n(X, A; G) \xrightarrow{\delta} \mathbf{C}^{n+1}(X, A; G)$$

is the trivial homomorphism; that is, $\delta \circ \delta = 0$.

Proof. Let ϕ denote an arbitrary element of $\mathbf{C}^{n-1}(X, A; G)$. Then ϕ is a homomorphism

$$\phi\colon \mathbf{C}_{n-1}(X, A) \rightarrow G.$$

Since $\delta = \text{Hom}(\partial, i)$, it follows from the definition of Hom in [H2, p. 110] that we have

$$
\begin{aligned}
(\delta \circ \delta)(\phi) &= \delta[\delta(\phi)] \\
&= \delta(\phi \circ \partial) \\
&= \phi \circ \partial \circ \partial = 0
\end{aligned}
$$

because of [H5, p. 192, (3.1)]. Since this holds for every element ϕ of $\mathbf{C}^{n-1}(X, A; G)$, it follows that

$$\delta \circ \delta = 0.$$

This completes the proof of (5.1). ‖

Thus we obtain a simiexact sequence

$$\cdots \to \mathbf{C}^{n-1}(X, A; G) \xrightarrow{\delta} \mathbf{C}^n(X, A; G) \xrightarrow{\delta} \mathbf{C}^{n+1}(X, A; G) \to \cdots$$

in the sense of [H2, p. 96], which will be denoted by

$$\mathbf{C}^*(X, A; G)$$

and called the *cochain complex* of (X, A) over G.

For every integer n, the kernel of the coboundary operator

$$\delta \colon \mathbf{C}^n(X, A; G) \to \mathbf{C}^{n+1}(X, A; G)$$

is called the *group of n-dimensional cocycles of* (X, A) *over* G and will be denoted by the symbol

$$\mathbf{Z}^n(X, A; G).$$

On the other hand, the image of the homomorphism

$$\delta \colon \mathbf{C}^{n-1}(X, A; G) \to \mathbf{C}^n(X, A; G)$$

is called the *group of n-dimensional coboundaries of* (X, A) *over* G and will be denoted by the symbol

$$\mathbf{B}^n(X, A; G).$$

Since $\mathbf{C}^*(X, A; G)$ is semiexact, it follows that

$$\mathbf{B}^n(X, A; G) \subset \mathbf{Z}^n(X, A; G)$$

holds. The quotient group

$$\mathbf{H}^n(X, A; G) = \mathbf{Z}^n(X, A; G)/\mathbf{B}^n(X, A; G)$$

is called the *n-dimensional cohomology group of the finite cellular pair* (X, A) *over* G.

For the special case $A = \square$, the group $\mathbf{H}^n(X; G)$ is called the *n-dimensional cohomology group of the finite cellular polytope* X *over* G.

Theorem 5.2. *If $\mathscr{H}$ is an arbitrary cohomology theory defined on an admissible category $\mathscr{C}$ which contains all finite cellular pairs and all maps of such pairs, then we have*

$$\mathbf{H}^n(X, A; G) \approx H^n(X, A)$$

for every finite cellular pair (X, A) and every integer n, provided that the Abelian group G is isomorphic to the coefficient group of the cohomology theory $\mathscr{H}$.

The proof of (5.2) is dual to that of [H5, p. 201, (4.5)] and hence is omitted.

As important consequences of (5.2), we have the following two corollaries.

Corollary 5.3 (*Uniqueness Theorem*). *For any two cohomology theories $\mathcal{H}$ and $\mathcal{H}'$ defined on admissible categories containing all finite cellular pairs and all maps of such pairs, we have*

$$H^n(X, A) \approx H'^n(X, A)$$

for every finite cellular pair (X, A) and every integer n, provided that the coefficient group of $\mathcal{H}$ is isomorphic to that of $\mathcal{H}'$.

Corollary 5.4 (*Invariance Theorem*). *For any two homotopically equivalent finite cellular pairs (X, A) and (Y, B), we have*

$$\mathbf{H}^n(X, A; G) \approx \mathbf{H}^n(Y, B; G)$$

for every Abelian group G and every integer n.

Thus, for any given Abelian group G and every integer n, the cohomology group $\mathbf{H}^n(X, A; G)$ of a finite cellular pair (X, A) depends only on the homotopy type of the topological pair (X, A). In other words, $\mathbf{H}^n(X, A; G)$ is a *homotopy invariant* of the finite cellular pair (X, A).

The remainder of the present section is devoted to the special case where

$$G = Z$$

is additive group of all integers. For this special case, the following simple notation,

$$\mathbf{H}^n(X, A) = \mathbf{H}^n(X, A; Z), \qquad \mathbf{C}^n(X, A) = \mathbf{C}^n(X, A; Z),$$

$$\mathbf{Z}^n(X, A) = \mathbf{Z}^n(X, A; Z), \qquad \mathbf{B}^n(X, A) = \mathbf{B}^n(X, A; Z),$$

is traditional. The group $\mathbf{H}^n(X, A)$ is called the *n-dimensional integral cohomology group of the finite cellular pair.*

For every integer n, let

$$\alpha_n(X, A) = m$$

denote the cardinality of $S_n(X, A)$, that is, the number of (open) n-cells in $X \setminus A$. In the case $m > 0$, let

$$\xi_1, \xi_2, \ldots, \xi_m$$

denote these n-cells. Since the group $C_n(X, A)$ of integral n-chains of (X, A) is a free Abelian group with $S_n(X, A)$ as a basis, we may define a homomorphism

$$\xi_i^*: C_n(X, A) \to Z$$

by taking

$$\xi_i^*(\xi_j) = \begin{cases} 1 & (\text{if } j = i), \\ 0 & (\text{if } j \neq i). \end{cases}$$

Then one can easily verify that the *group* $C^n(X, A)$ *of n-dimensional integral cochains* of (X, A) is a free Abelian group with

$$\{\xi_1^*, \xi_2^*, \ldots, \xi_m^*\}$$

as a basis.

Next consider the coboundary operator

$$\delta: C^{n-1}(X, A) \to C^n(X, A).$$

Assume $\alpha_{n-1}(X, A) = l$ and let

$$\eta_1, \eta_2, \ldots, \eta_l$$

denote the $(n-1)$-cells in $X \setminus A$. Then one can easily verify that

$$\delta(\eta_j^*) = \sum_{i=1}^{m} [\xi_i, \eta_j] \, \xi_i^*$$

holds for every $j = 1, 2, \ldots, l$, where $[\xi_i, \eta_j]$ denotes the *incidence number* defined in [H5, pp. 179–181]. The m by l matrix

$$M_n = M_n(X, A)$$

of integers with $[\xi_i, \eta_j]$ as its element at its ith row and its jth column is defined in [H5, p. 189] as the *n-dimensional incidence matrix* of the finite cellular pair (X, A). Let

$$r(M_n)$$

denote the rank of the matrix M_n.

As a quotient group of a subgroup of a finitely generated free Abelian group $C^n(X, A)$, the n-dimensional integral cohomology group $H^n(X, A)$ is finitely generated. Its rank and its torsion coefficients are given by the following theorem.

Theorem 5.5. *For every integer n, the rank of* $H^n(X, A)$ *is equal to*

$$\alpha_n(X, A) - r(M_n) - r(M_{n+1}),$$

and the torsion coefficients of $H^n(X,A)$ *are those invariant factors of the incidence matrix* $M_n(X,A)$ *which are greater than* 1.

The proof of (5.5) is dual to that of [H5, p. 196, (3.8) and (3.9)] and hence is omitted.

The following corollaries are immediate consequences of (5.5) and [H5, p. 196, (3.8) and (3.9)].

Corollary 5.6. *The rank of* $H^n(X,A)$ *is equal to the n-dimensional Betti number* $\beta_n(X,A)$ *of* (X,A), *that is, the rank of* $H_n(X,A)$.

Corollary 5.7. *The torsion coefficients of* $H^n(X,A)$ *are equal to the* $(n-1)$*-dimensional torsion coefficients of* (X,A), *that is, the torsion coefficients of* $H_{n-1}(X,A)$.

EXERCISES
5A. Find the integral cohomology groups of the following finite cellular polytopes:
   (a) n-sphere,
   (b) orientable closed surfaces,
   (c) nonorientable closed surfaces,
   (d) lens spaces,
   (e) real projective n -spaces.
5B. For an arbitrary finite cellular pair (X,A) and any given field G, prove that the cohomology group $H^n(X,A;G)$ is a vector space over G of finite dimension for every n. Find the dimension of $H^2(X,A;G)$ when:
   (a) G is of characteristic 0;
   (b) G is of characteristic p.

Chapter 2

SINGULAR COHOMOLOGY THEORY

THE PRESENT CHAPTER is devoted to the construction of the *singular cohomology theory*. Several proofs are omitted since they are dual to those in singular homology theory given in [H5]. On the other hand, since proofs of the *homotopy axiom* and the *excision axiom* for singular homology theory were not given in [H5], we shall present detailed verifications for these two axioms. Similar methods can be used to verify the axioms for the singular homology theory.

1. Singular Complex of a Space

The singular theory of homology and cohomology is constructed by means of (continuous) maps of the *unit n-simplex* Δ_n of the $(n+1)$-dimensional Euclidean space R^{n+1} for all nonnegative integers n, which is defined as the subspace of R^{n+1} consisting of all points $(x_0, x_1, \ldots, x_n)$ of R^{n+1} such that

$$\sum_{i=0}^{n} x_i = 1, \qquad x_i \geq 0, \qquad (i = 0, 1, \ldots, n).$$

For each integer $i = 0, 1, \ldots, n$, the point

$$v_i = (\delta_{i0}, \delta_{i1}, \ldots, \delta_{in})$$

of R^{n+1} with

$$\delta_{ij} = \begin{cases} 1 & \text{(if } i = j), \\ 0 & \text{(if } i \neq j), \end{cases}$$

is a point of Δ_n and will be called the *ith vertex* of Δ_n. The unit n-simplex

37

Δ_n has $n + 1$ vertices $v_0, v_1, \ldots, v_n$ and is the convex hull of the set

$$V = \{v_0, v_1, \ldots, v_n\}.$$

For each integer $i = 0, 1, \ldots, n$, the subspace

$$\Delta_n^{(i)} = \{(x_0, x_1, \ldots, x_n) \in \Delta_n \mid x_i = 0\}$$

of the unit n-simplex Δ_n is called the *ith face* of Δ_n or the *face of Δ_n opposite* to the ith vertex v_i.

Assume $n > 0$ and consider the map

$$\kappa_i \colon \Delta_{n-1} \to \Delta_n$$

for every $i = 0, 1, \ldots, n$ defined by

$$\kappa_i(x_0, \ldots, x_{n-1}) = (x_0, \ldots, x_{i-1}, 0, x_i, \ldots, x_{n-1})$$

for each point $(x_0, \ldots, x_{n-1})$ of Δ_{n-1}. Then κ_i is an imbedding of Δ_{n-1} into Δ_n and its image

$$\kappa_i(\Delta_{n-1}) = \Delta_n^{(i)}$$

is the ith face of Δ_n. Next assume $n > 1$ and consider the imbeddings

$$\Delta_{n-2} \xrightarrow{\kappa_j} \Delta_{n-1} \xrightarrow{\kappa_i} \Delta_n$$

where $0 \leq i \leq n$ and $0 \leq j \leq n - 1$.

Lemma 1.1. *If $0 \leq j < i \leq n$, then we have*

$$\kappa_i \circ \kappa_j = \kappa_j \circ \kappa_{i-1} \colon \Delta_{n-2} \to \Delta_n.$$

For a proof of (1.1), see [H5, p. 206].

Now let X denote an arbitrary topological space and n any nonnegative integer. By a *singular n-simplex* in X, we mean a (continuous) map

$$\xi \colon \Delta_n \to X$$

of the unit n-simplex Δ_n into the given space X. Let

$$S_n(X) = \operatorname{Map}(\Delta_n, X)$$

denote the set of all singular n-simplexes in X. If $m \neq n$, then by definition we have

$$S_m(X) \cap S_n(X) = \square.$$

The union

$$S(X) = \bigcup_{n=0}^{\infty} S_n(X)$$

is the set of all singular simplexes in the given space X and will be referred to as the *singular complex* of X.

Assume $n > 0$ and let

$$\xi: \Delta_n \to X$$

denote any singular n-simplex in X. For every integer $i = 0, 1, \ldots, n$, the composed map

$$\xi^{(i)} = \xi \circ \kappa_i: \Delta_{n-1} \to X$$

is a singular $(n - 1)$-simplex in X, which will be called the ith *face* of ξ. The $n + 1$ faces $\xi^{(0)}, \ldots, \xi^{(n)}$ of a singular n-simplex ξ in X might not be distinct. In fact, if $\xi: \Delta_n \to X$ is a constant map, then all its $n + 1$ faces $\xi^{(0)}, \ldots, \xi^{(n)}$ are the same singular $(n - 1)$-simplex of X.

The following proposition is a direct consequence of (1.1).

Proposition 1.2. *If $n > 1$ and $0 \leqslant j < i \leqslant n$, then we have*

$$[\xi^{(i)}]^{(j)} = [\xi^{(j)}]^{(i-1)}$$

for every singular n-simplex ξ in X.

Now let us consider an arbitrary subspace A of the given space X with inclusion map

$$\iota: A \to X.$$

Every singular n-simplex $\xi: \Delta_n \to A$ in the subspace A of X can be identified with the singular n-simplex

$$\iota \circ \xi: \Delta_n \to X$$

of the given space X. Thus we have

$$S_n(A) \subset S_n(X), \qquad S(A) \subset S(X).$$

Furthermore, for every singular n-simplex ξ in X with $n > 0$, $\xi \in S_n(A)$ implies $\xi^{(i)} \in S_{n-1}(A)$ for every $i = 0, 1, \ldots, n$. Because of this property, $S(A)$ is said to be a *subcomplex* of the singular complex $S(X)$.

For every nonnegative integer n, let $C_n(X)$ denote the free Abelian group generated by the set $S_n(X)$ as defined in [H2, p. 81]. Then we have

$$S_n(X) \subset C_n(X).$$

For each $n > 0$, define a function

$$\sigma: S_n(X) \to C_{n-1}(X)$$

by taking

$$\sigma(\xi) = \sum_{i=0}^{n} (-1)^i \xi^{(i)}$$

for every singular n-simplex $\xi\colon \Delta_n \to X$. Since $C_n(X)$ is the free Abelian group generated by the set $S_n(X)$, it follows from [H2, p. 81] that σ extends to a unique homomorphism

$$\partial\colon C_n(X) \to C_{n-1}(X)$$

which will be referred to as the *boundary operator*. For completeness, we also define

$$C_n(X) = 0$$

for all integers $n < 0$ and define

$$\partial\colon C_n(X) \to C_{n-1}(X)$$

as the trivial homomorphism whenever $n \leqslant 0$.

Proposition 1.3. *For every integer n, the composed homomorphism*

$$\partial^2 = \partial \circ \partial\colon C_n(X) \to C_{n-2}(X)$$

of the boundary operators

$$C_n(X) \xrightarrow{\ \partial\ } C_{n-1}(X) \xrightarrow{\ \partial\ } C_{n-2}(X)$$

is a trivial homomorphism—in symbols, $\partial^2 = 0$.
For a proof of (1.3), see [H5, p. 211].
Thus we obtain a *semiexact sequence*

$$\cdots \to C_{n+1}(X) \xrightarrow{\ \partial\ } C_n(X) \xrightarrow{\ \partial\ } C_{n-1}(X) \to \cdots$$

in the sense of [H2, p. 96], which will be referred to as the *integral singular chain complex* of the space X and which will be denoted by the symbol $C(X)$.

Now consider an arbitrary subspace A of the given space X. Since $S_n(A)$ is a subset of $S_n(X)$, it follows that $C_n(A)$ is the direct summand of $C_n(X)$ generated by the set $S_n(A)$. Furthermore, one can easily see that the boundary operator

$$\partial\colon C_n(X) \to C_{n-1}(X)$$

sends the subgroup $C_n(A)$ of $C_n(X)$ into the subgroup $C_{n-1}(A)$ of $C_{n-1}(X)$. Because of this, $C(A)$ is said to be a *subcomplex* of the integral singular chain complex $C(X)$.

EXERCISES

1A. Show that $S_0(X)$ can be considered as X itself.

1B. Show that $S_1(X)$ can be identified with the set $P(X)$ of all paths in the space X.

1C. In the case $X = \square$, show that $C_n(X) = 0$ for every integer n.

1D. Assume that X is a singleton space. Then, for every $n \geqslant 0$, $S_n(X)$ consists of a single singular n-simplex

$$\xi_n : \Delta_n \to X,$$

and $C_n(X)$ is the infinite cyclic group generated by ξ_n. Prove that

$$\partial : C_n(X) \to C_{n-1}(X)$$

is an isomorphism if n is a positive even integer and is a trivial homomorphism otherwise.

2. Singular Cohomology Groups over G

Let X denote an arbitrarily given topological space and G any Abelian group.

Consider the integral singular chain complex $C(X)$ of X as defined in the preceding section. For every integer n, let

$$C^n(X; G) = \mathrm{Hom}[C_n(X), G]$$

denote the Abelian group of all homomorphisms of $C_n(X)$ into G as defined in [H2, p. 109]. This group $C^n(X; G)$ is called the *n-dimensional singular cochain group of X over G*.

For every $n < 0$, we have

$$C^n(X; G) = 0$$

because of $C_n(X) = 0$. For $n \geqslant 0$, since $C_n(X)$ is the free Abelian group generated by the set $S_n(X)$ of all n-dimensional singular simplexes in X, it follows that the assignment $\phi \to \phi | S_n(X)$ defines an isomorphism

$$\iota : \mathrm{Hom}[C_n(X), G] \approx \mathrm{Fun}[S_n(X), G]$$

from $\mathrm{Hom}[C_n(X), G]$ onto the Abelian group $\mathrm{Fun}[S_n(X), G]$ of all functions from $S_n(X)$ into G. Hence the elements of $C^n(X; G)$, which are called the *n-dimensional singular cochains of X over G*, can also be considered as the functions defined on $S_n(X)$ with values in G.

Now, for every integer n, consider the boundary operator

$$\partial : C_n(X) \to C_{n-1}(X)$$

of $C(X)$ and the identity automorphism

$$i: G \to G$$

of the Abelian group G. The homomorphism

$$\text{Hom}(\partial, i): \text{Hom}[C_{n-1}(X), G] \to \text{Hom}[C_n(X), G]$$

as defined in [H2, p. 110] will be simply denoted by

$$\delta: C^{n-1}(X; G) \to C^n(X; G)$$

and will be referred to as the *coboundary* operator on the group $C^{n-1}(X; G)$.

If $n \leq 0$, then $C^{n-1}(X; G) = 0$ and hence $\delta = 0$. Assume $n > 0$ and let $\phi \in C^{n-1}(X; G)$. Then

$$\phi: C_{n-1}(X) \to G$$

is a homomorphism and, by the definition in [H2, p. 110], $\delta(\phi) \in C^n(X; G)$ is the composition

$$\delta(\phi) = \phi \circ \partial: C_n(X) \to G.$$

For every singular n-simplex ξ in X, we have

$$[\delta(\phi)](\xi) = \phi[\partial(\xi)] = \phi\left[\sum_{i=0}^{n} (-1)^i \xi^{(i)}\right] = \sum_{i=0}^{n} (-1)^i \phi[\xi^{(i)}].$$

Proposition 2.1. *The composition $\delta \circ \delta$ of the coboundary operators*

$$C^{n-1}(X; G) \xrightarrow{\ \delta\ } C^n(X; G) \xrightarrow{\ \delta\ } C^{n+1}(X; G)$$

is the trivial homomorphism of $C^{n-1}(X; G)$ into $C^{n+1}(X; G)$; in symbols, $\delta \circ \delta = 0$.

Proof. Let $\phi \in C^{n-1}(X; G)$ be arbitrarily given. Then we have

$$(\delta \circ \delta)(\phi) = \delta[\delta(\phi)] = \delta(\phi \circ \partial) = \phi \circ \partial \circ \partial = 0,$$

since $\partial \circ \partial = 0$ according to (1.3). This proves (2.1). $\|$

Thus we obtain a *semiexact upper sequence*

$$\cdots \to C^{n-1}(X; G) \xrightarrow{\ \delta\ } C^n(X; G) \xrightarrow{\ \delta\ } C^{n+1}(X; G) \to \cdots$$

in the sense of [H2, p. 97], which will be referred to as the *singular cochain complex of X over G* and will be denoted by the symbol

$$C^*(X; G).$$

For every integer n, the kernel of the coboundary operator

$$\delta: C^n(X; G) \to C^{n+1}(X; G)$$

is called the *group of n-dimensional singular cocycles* of X over G and will be denoted by the symbol

$$Z^n(X; G).$$

On the other hand, the image of the coboundary operator

$$\delta: C^{n-1}(X; G) \to C^n(X; G)$$

is called the *group of n-dimensional singular coboundaries* of X over G and will be denoted by the symbol

$$B^n(X; G).$$

Since $C^*(X; G)$ is semiexact, it follows that the inclusion

$$B^n(X; G) \subset Z^n(X; G)$$

holds. The quotient group

$$H^n(X; G) = Z^n(X; G)/B^n(X; G)$$

is called the *n-dimensional singular cohomology group* of the given space X over the Abelian group G.

In particular, if G is the group Z of all integers, then the group

$$H^n(X) = H^n(X; Z)$$

is called the *n-dimensional integral singular cohomology group of the space X*.

Now let us consider an arbitrary subspace A of the given space X. The subgroup

$$C^n(X, A; G) = \{\phi \in C^n(X; G) | \phi[C_n(A)] = 0\}$$

of $C^n(X; G)$ is called the *n-dimensional singular cochain group of the topological pair (X, A) over G*. The elements of $C^n(X, A; G)$ are called the *singular n-cochains of (X, A) over G* or the *singular n-cochains of X modulo A over G*.

From its very definition, one can easily see that the coboundary operator

$$\delta: C^{n-1}(X; G) \to C^n(X; G)$$

sends the subgroup $C^{n-1}(X, A; G)$ of $C^{n-1}(X; G)$ into the subgroup $C^n(X, A; G)$ of $C^n(X; G)$. Hence it defines a homomorphism of the group $C^{n-1}(X, A; G)$ into the group $C^n(X, A; G)$, which will be denoted by

$$\delta: C^{n-1}(X, A; G) \to C^n(X, A; G).$$

Then $\delta \circ \delta = 0$ is obviously satisfied. Hence we obtain a semiexact upper sequence

$$\cdots \to C^{n-1}(X, A; G) \xrightarrow{\delta} C^n(X, A; G) \xrightarrow{\delta} C^{n+1}(X, A; G) \to \cdots$$

which will be referred to as the *singular cochain complex of* (X, A) *over* G and will be denoted by the symbol

$$C^*(X, A; G).$$

The following special case is obvious:

$$C^*(X, \Box; G) = C^*(X; G).$$

For every integer n, the kernel of the coboundary operator

$$\delta: C^n(X, A; G) \to C^{n+1}(X, A; G)$$

is called the *group of n-dimensional singular cocycles of* (X, A) *over* G and will be denoted by the term

$$Z^n(X, A; G).$$

On the other hand, the image of the coboundary operator

$$\delta: C^{n-1}(X, A; G) \to C^n(X, A; G)$$

is called the *group of n-dimensional singular coboundaries of* (X, A) *over* G and will be denoted by the symbol

$$B^n(X, A; G).$$

Since $C^*(X, A; G)$ is semiexact, it follows that the inclusion

$$B^n(X, A; G) \subset Z^n(X, A; G)$$

holds. The quotient group

$$H^n(X, A; G) = Z^n(X, A; G)/B^n(X, A; G)$$

is called the *n-dimensional singular cohomology group of the topological pair* (X, A) *over the Abelian group* G, or the *n-dimensional singular cohomology group of X modulo A over G*.

The following special case is obvious:

$$H^n(X, \Box; G) = H^n(X; G).$$

In particular, if G is the group Z of all integers, then the group

$$H^n(X,A) = H^n(X,A;Z)$$

is called the *n-dimensional integral singular cohomology group of X modulo A*.

Finally, since $C^n(X,A;G) = 0$ holds obviously for every $n < 0$, we have the following proposition.

Proposition 2.2. *If $n < 0$, then we have*

$$H^n(X,A;G) = 0$$

for every topological pair (X,A) and every Abelian group G.

EXERCISES

2A. Let X be a topological space which consists of a single point. Prove that

$$H^n(X;G) \approx \begin{cases} G & (\text{if } n = 0), \\ 0 & (\text{if } n \neq 0). \end{cases}$$

2B. Prove that the zero-dimensional singular cohomology group $H^0(X;G)$ of a space X over G is isomorphic to the group Φ of all functions $f: \pi_0(X) \to G$ from the set $\pi_0(X)$ of all path-components of X into G.

2C. For every element $g \in G$, prove that the zero-dimensional singular cochain

$$\phi_g: C_0(X) \to G$$

defined by $\phi_g(\sigma) = g$ for every σ in $C_0(X)$ is a cocycle and hence represents an element $\epsilon(g)$ of the group $H^0(X;G)$. Prove that the assignment $g \to \epsilon(g)$ defines a monomorphism

$$\epsilon: G \to H^0(X;G)$$

known as the *augmentation*.

3. Induced Homomorphisms and Coboundary Operators

Let (X,A) and (Y,B) denote topological pairs and consider an arbitrarily given (continuous) map

$$f: (X,A) \to (Y,B).$$

For every $n \geq 0$, f induces a function

$$S_n(f): S_n(X) \to S_n(Y)$$

defined by

$$[S_n(f)](\xi) = f \circ \xi \colon \Delta_n \to Y$$

for every n-dimensional singular simplex $\xi \colon \Delta_n \to X$ in X. Since $f(A) \subset B$, it follows that $S_n(f)$ sends $S_n(A)$ into $S_n(B)$.

Since $C_n(X)$ is the free Abelian group generated by $S_n(X)$, this function

$$S_n(f) \colon S_n(X) \to S_n(Y) \subset C_n(Y)$$

extends to a unique homomorphism

$$C_n(f) \colon C_n(X) \to C_n(Y).$$

Since $S_n(f)$ sends $S_n(A)$ into $S_n(B)$, it is obvious that $C_n(f)$ sends $C_n(A)$ into $C_n(B)$.

For every negative integer n, we have $C_n(X) = 0$ and $C_n(Y) = 0$; in this case, let $C_n(f)$ denote the trivial homomorphism. Thus the homomorphism

$$C_n(f) \colon [C_n(X), C_n(A)] \to [C_n(Y), C_n(B)]$$

is defined for every integer n.

Lemma 3.1. *The rectangle*

$$
\begin{CD}
C_n(X) @>\partial_X>> C_{n-1}(X) \\
@V C_n(f) VV @VV C_{n-1}(f) V \\
C_n(Y) @>\partial_Y>> C_{n-1}(Y)
\end{CD}
$$

of homomorphisms, where ∂_X and ∂_Y stand for the boundary operators, is commutative; that is,

$$\partial_Y \circ C_n(f) = C_{n-1}(f) \circ \partial_X.$$

For a proof of (3.1), see [H5, p. 227].

Next, let G denote an arbitrary Abelian group and consider the singular cochain complexes $C^*(X; G)$ and $C^*(Y; G)$. For every integer n, the homomorphism

$$\mathrm{Hom}[C_n(f), i] \colon C^n(Y; G) \to C^n(X; G),$$

where $i \colon G \to G$ denotes the identity automorphism, obviously sends the subgroup $C^n(Y, B; G)$ of $C^n(Y; G)$ into the subgroup $C^n(X, A; G)$ of $C^n(X; G)$ and hence defines a homomorphism

$$C^n(f; G) \colon C^n(Y, B; G) \to C^n(X, A; G).$$

It follows from the definition of $\operatorname{Hom}[C_n(f), G]$ in [H2, p. 109] that, for every $\xi\colon C_n(Y) \to G$ in $C^n(Y, B; G)$, we have

$$[C^n(f; G)]\,(\xi) = \xi \circ C_n(f)\colon C_n(X) \to G.$$

The following proposition is a direct consequence of (3.1).

Proposition 3.2. *The rectangle*

$$\begin{array}{ccc}
C^{n-1}(Y, B; G) & \xrightarrow{\delta_Y} & C^n(Y, B; G) \\
\downarrow{\scriptstyle C^{n-1}(f;G)} & & \downarrow{\scriptstyle C^n(f;G)} \\
C^{n-1}(X, A; G) & \xrightarrow{\delta_X} & C^n(X, A; G)
\end{array}$$

of homomorphisms, where δ_X and δ_Y stand for the coboundary operators, is commutative; that is,

$$\delta_X \circ C^{n-1}(f; G) = C^n(f; G) \circ \delta_Y.$$

Thus we obtain the following ladder:

$$\begin{array}{ccccccc}
\cdots \to C^{n-1}(Y, B; G) & \xrightarrow{\delta_Y} & C^n(Y, B; G) & \xrightarrow{\delta_Y} & C^{n+1}(Y, B; G) & \to \cdots \\
\downarrow{\scriptstyle C^{n+1}(f;G)} & & \downarrow{\scriptstyle C^n(f;G)} & & \downarrow{\scriptstyle C^{n+1}(f;G)} & \\
\cdots \to C^{n-1}(X, A; G) & \xrightarrow{\delta_X} & C^n(X, A; G) & \xrightarrow{\delta_X} & C^{n+1}(X, A; G) & \to \cdots
\end{array}$$

Here the two horizontal rows are the singular cochain complexes $C^*(X, A; G)$ and $C^*(Y, B; G)$, and hence are semiexact. According to (3.2), the rectangles are commutative. Because of this, the sequence of homomorphisms

$$C^*(f; G) = \{C^n(f; G) \mid n \in Z\}$$

is called the *cochain transformation*

$$C^*(f; G)\colon C^*(Y, B; G) \to C^*(X, A; G)$$

induced by the given map $f\colon (X, A) \to (Y, B)$.

Proposition 3.3. *For every integer n, the homomorphism*

$$C^n(f; G)\colon C^n(Y, B; G) \to C^n(X, A; G)$$

sends $Z^n(Y, B; G)$ into $Z^n(X, A; G)$ and $B^n(Y, B; G)$ into $B^n(X, A; G)$.

The proof of (3.3) is dual to that of [H5, p. 228, (5.3)] and hence is omitted.

From (3.3), it follows that $C^n(f; G)$ induces a homomorphism

$$f^* = H^n(f; G): H^n(Y, B; G) \to H^n(X, A; G)$$

which will be referred to as the *induced homomorphism* of the given map

$$f: (X, A) \to (Y, B)$$

on the *n*-dimensional singular cohomology group $H^n(Y, B; G)$.

The following properties of the induced homomorphisms are obvious from the definition.

Proposition 3.4. *If i: $(X, A) \to (X, A)$ is the identity map on a topological pair (X, A), then the induced homomorphism*

$$i^* = H^n(i; G): H^n(X, A; G) \to H^n(X, A; G)$$

is the identity automorphism on $H^n(X, A; G)$ for every integer n and every Abelian group G.

Proposition 3.5. *For arbitrary maps*

$$f: (X, A) \to (Y, B), \qquad g: (Y, B) \to (Z, C)$$

of topological pairs (X, A), (Y, B), and (Z, C), we have

$$H^n(g \circ f; G) = H^n(f; G) \circ H^n(g; G)$$

for every integer n and every Abelian group G.

Let (X, A) denote any topological pair and G an arbitrary Abelian group. Our objective in the remainder of this section is to construct for each integer *n* a homomorphism

$$\delta: H^{n-1}(A; G) \to H^n(X, A; G),$$

which will be called the *coboundary operator* of the pair (X, A) on the group $H^{n-1}(A; G)$.

For this purpose, let us first define a function

$$\phi: Z^{n-1}(A; G) \to H^n(X, A; G)$$

as follows. Let z denote an arbitrary element of $Z^{n-1}(A; G)$. As an element of $C^{n-1}(A; G)$. z is a homomorphism

$$z: C_{n-1}(A) \to G.$$

Since $C_{n-1}(A)$ is a direct summand of $C_{n-1}(X)$, there exists a homomorphism

$$u: C_{n-1}(X) \to G$$

satisfying $u|C_{n-1}(A) = z$. By definition, u is an element of $C^{n-1}(X; G)$. Consider the element

$$\delta(u) \in C^n(X; G),$$

where $\delta: C^{n-1}(X; G) \to C^n(X; G)$ denotes the coboundary operator on $C^{n-1}(X; G)$.

Lemma 3.6. *The element $\delta(u)$ is contained in the subgroup $Z^n(X, A; G)$ of the group $C^n(X; G)$.*

Proof. To prove $\delta(u) \in C^n(X, A; G)$, let c denote an arbitrary element in $C_n(A)$. Then we have

$$[\delta(u)](c) = u[\partial(c)] = z[\partial(c)] = [\delta(z)](c) = 0,$$

since $\partial(c) \in C_{n-1}(A)$ and $z \in Z^{n-1}(A; G)$. This implies $\delta(u) \in C^n(X, A; G)$. On the other hand, we have

$$\delta[\delta(u)] = (\delta \circ \delta)(u) = 0.$$

Hence $\delta(u) \in Z^n(X, A; G)$. $\|$

Consider the natural projection

$$p: Z^n(X, A; G) \to H^n(X, A; G)$$

of $Z^n(X, A; G)$ onto its quotient group

$$H^n(X, A; G) = Z^n(X, A; G)/B^n(X, A; G).$$

Lemma 3.7. *The element $p[\delta(u)]$ of $H^n(X, A; G)$ is independent of the choice of $u \in C^{n-1}(X; G)$ and hence depends only on the element $z \in Z^{n-1}(A; G)$.*

Proof. Let u and v denote any two elements of $C^{n-1}(X; G)$ satisfying

$$u \mid C_{n-1}(A) = z = v \mid C_{n-1}(A).$$

It suffices to prove that $p[\delta(u)] = p[\delta(v)]$.

For this purpose, let us consider the element $u - v$ of $C^{n-1}(X; G)$. Since

$$(u - v)|C_{n-1}(A) = z - z = 0,$$

it follows that $u - v$ is contained in the subgroup $C^{n-1}(X, A; G)$ of $C^{n-1}(X; G)$. This implies that the element $\delta(u - v)$ is in $B^n(X, A; G)$ and hence

$$p[\delta(u)] - p[\delta(v)] = p[\delta(u - v)] = 0.$$

This proves that $p[\delta(u)] = p[\delta(v)]$.   ‖

Because of (3.7), we may define the function

$$\phi: Z^{n-1}(A; G) \to H^n(X, A; G)$$

by assigning to each element z of $Z^{n-1}(A; G)$ the element

$$\phi(z) = p[\partial(u)] \in H^n(X, A; G)$$

with any $u \in C^{n-1}(X; G)$ satisfying $u \mid C_{n-1}(A) = z$.

Lemma 3.8. *This function ϕ is a homomorphism of $Z^{n+1}(A; G)$ into $H^n(X, A; G)$.*

The proof of (3.8) is similar to that of [H5, p. 232, (6.4)] and hence is omitted.

Lemma 3.9. *The kernel of this homomorphism ϕ contains the subgroup $B^{n-1}(A; G)$ of $Z^{n-1}(A; G)$.*

Proof. Let z denote an arbitrary element of $B^{n-1}(A; G)$. By definition, there exists an element y of $C^{n-2}(A; G)$ with $\delta(y) = z$. Select any element $v \in C^{n-2}(X; G)$ with $v \mid C_{n-2}(A) = y$. Then the element

$$u = \delta(v) \in C^{n-1}(X; G)$$

satisfies $u \mid C_{n-1}(A) = z$. Hence we have

$$\phi(z) = p[\delta(u) = p[\delta^2(v)] = 0.$$

This completes the proof of (3.9).   ‖

Because of (3.9), the homomorphism

$$\phi: Z^{n-1}(A; G) \to H^n(X, A; G)$$

induces a homomorphism

$$\delta: H^{n-1}(A; G) \to H^n(X, A; G),$$

which is called the *coboundary operator* for the pair (X, A) on the group $H^{n-1}(A; G)$.

Now let us consider an arbitrarily given map

$$f: (X, A) \to (Y, B)$$

of a topological pair (X, A) into a topological pair (Y, B). Let

$$g: A \to B$$

denote the map defined by f. Then we have the following proposition.

Proposition 3.10. *For every integer n and every Abelian group G, the rectangle*

$$
\begin{array}{ccc}
H^{n-1}(B; G) & \xrightarrow{\delta} & H^n(Y, B; G) \\
\downarrow{g^*} & & \downarrow{f^*} \\
H^{n-1}(A; G) & \xrightarrow{\delta} & H^n(X, A; G)
\end{array}
$$

is commutative; that is, we have

$$\delta \circ g^* = f^* \circ \delta.$$

The proof of (3.10) is dual to that of [H5, p. 233, (6.6)] and hence is omitted.

Finally, let (X, A) denote an arbitrary topological pair and G any given Abelian group.

Consider the inclusion maps

$$i: A \to X, \qquad j: X \to (X, A).$$

These inclusion maps induce homomorphisms

$$i^*: H^n(X; G) \to H^n(A; G),$$

$$j^*: H^n(X, A; G) \to H^n(X; G)$$

for every integer n. On the other hand, we also have the coboundary operator

$$\delta: H^{n-1}(A; G) \to H^n(X, A; G)$$

defined for every integer n.

Thus we obtain an upper sequence

$$\cdots \to H^{n-1}(A; G) \xrightarrow{\delta} H^n(X, A; G) \xrightarrow{j^*} H^n(X; G) \xrightarrow{i^*} H^n(A; G) \to \cdots$$

which will be called the *singular cohomology sequence of* (X, A) *over* G.

Proposition 3.11. *The singular cohomology sequence of (X, A) over G is exact.*

The proof of (3.11) is dual to that of [H5, p. 236, (7.1)] and hence is omitted.

EXERCISES

3A. A subspace X of a Euclidean space E is said to be *starlike* iff there exists a point $x_0 \in X$ such that, for every $x \in X$, X contains the closed line segment $[x_0, x]$. Let X denote any topological space which is homeomorphic to a starlike subspace of a Euclidean space. Prove that the sequence

$$\cdots \to C_n(X) \xrightarrow{\partial} C_{n-1}(X) \xrightarrow{\partial} \cdots \xrightarrow{\partial} C_1(X) \xrightarrow{\partial} C_0(X)$$

is exact. Then deduce that

$$H^n(X; G) \approx \begin{cases} G & \text{(if } n = 0) \\ 0 & \text{(if } n \neq 0) \end{cases}$$

for every Abelian group G.

4. Verification of Axioms

Consider the admissible category $\mathscr{C}_T$ of all topological pairs (X, A) and all maps of such pairs. Let G denote an arbitrary Abelian group. Define a collection of three functions

$$\mathscr{H} = \{H, *, \delta\}$$

as follows. For the first function H, we assign to each topological pair (X, A) and each integer q the *q-dimensional singular cohomology group*

$$H^q(X, A; G)$$

of the topological pair (X, A) over G. For the second function $*$, we assign to each map $f: (X, A) \to (Y, B)$ in $\mathscr{C}_T$ and each integer q the *induced homomorphism*

$$f^*: H^q(Y, B; G) \to H^q(X, A; G).$$

For the third function δ, we assign to each topological pair (X, A) and each integer q the *coboundary operator*

$$\delta: H^{q-1}(A; G) \to H^q(X, A; G).$$

To establish that this collection $\mathscr{H}$ is a cohomology theory on the category $\mathscr{C}_T$, we have to verify the seven Eilenberg-Steenrod axioms.

By (3.4) and (3.5), $\mathscr{H}$ satisfies the identity axiom (I) and the composition axiom (II). Because of (3.10), $\mathscr{H}$ satisfies the commutativity axiom (III). In view of (3.11), $\mathscr{H}$ satisfies the exactness axiom (IV). It remains to verify axioms V through VII.

To verify the homotopy axiom (V), it suffices to prove that, for any topological pair (X, A), the two canonical imbeddings

$$\kappa_0, \kappa_1 \colon (X, A) \to (X, A) \times I,$$

defined by $\kappa_o(x) = (x, 0)$ and $\kappa_1(x) = (x, 1)$ for every $x \in X$, induce the same homomorphism

$$\kappa_0^* = \kappa_1^* \colon H^q(X \times I, A \times I; G) \to H^q(X, A; G)$$

for every integer q in accordance with Exercise 1A, Chap. 1.

For this purpose, let us establish the following lemma.

Lemma 4.1. *For every topological space X and every integer n, there exists a homomorphism*

$$D_n \colon C_n(X) \to C_{n+1}(X \times I)$$

satisfying the following three conditions:

(a) *For every integer n and every element c of $C_n(X)$, we have*

$$\partial[D_n(c)] + D_{n-1}[\partial(c)] = [C_n(\kappa_1)](c) - [C_n(\kappa_0)](c).$$

(b) *For every subspace A of X, D_n sends the subgroup $C_n(A)$ of $C_n(X)$ into the subgroup $C_{n+1}(A \times I)$ of $C_{n+1}(X \times I)$.*

(c) *For every map $f \colon X \to Y$ and every integer n, the following rectangle is commutative*:

$$
\begin{array}{ccc}
C_n(X) & \xrightarrow{\ D_n\ } & C_{n+1}(X \times I) \\
\downarrow{\scriptstyle C_n(f)} & & \downarrow{\scriptstyle C_{n+1}(f \times i)} \\
C_n(Y) & \xrightarrow{\ D_n\ } & C_{n+1}(Y \times I)
\end{array}
$$

where $i \colon I \to I$ denotes the identity map.

Proof. First consider all $n < 0$. Since $C_n(X) = 0$ for every topological space X, we must have

$$D_n = 0.$$

The conditions (a) through (c) are obviously satisfied for every $n < 0$.

Next consider $n = 0$. Let X denote any topological space. For every singular 0-simplex ξ: $\Delta_0 \to X$, let $F_0(\xi)$ denote the singular 1-simplex

$$F_0(\xi): \Delta_1 \to X \times I$$

defined by

$$[F_0(\xi)](x_0, x_1) = [\xi(\Delta_0), x_1]$$

for every point (x_0, x_1) of the unit 1-simplex Δ_1. The assignment $\xi \to F_0(\xi)$ defines a function

$$F_0: S_0(X) \to C_1(X \times I).$$

Since $C_0(X)$ is the free Abelian group generated by $S_0(X)$, F_0 extends to a unique homomorphism

$$D_0: C_0(X) \to C_1(X \times I).$$

It is straightforward to verify that the conditions (a) through (c) are satisfied for all $n \leqslant 0$.

Finally, let us complete the construction by induction. For this purpose, let $q > 0$ be any positive integer such that, for every $n < q$, D_n is constructed for all topological spaces X in such a way that conditions (a) through (c) are satisfied.

Consider the identity map

$$i_q: \Delta_q \to \Delta_q$$

as a singular q-simplex of the space Δ_q and hence as an element of the group $C_q(\Delta_q)$. Since $\partial(\iota_q) \in C_{q-1}(\Delta_q)$, it follows from our inductive assumption (a) that

$$[C_{q-1}(\kappa_1)](\partial \iota_q) - [C_{q-1}(\kappa_0)](\partial \iota_q) = \partial[D_{q-1}(\partial \iota_q)]$$

because of $\partial(\partial \iota_q) = 0$. On the other hand, we have

$$\partial\{[C_q(\kappa_1)](\iota_q) - [C_q(\kappa_0)](\iota_q)\} = [C_{q-1}(\kappa_1)](\partial \iota_q) - [C_{q-1}(\kappa_0)](\partial \iota_q)$$

because of (3.1). It follows that the element

$$[C_q(\kappa_1)](\iota_q) - [C_q(\kappa_0)](\iota_q) - D_{q-1}[\partial(\iota_q)]$$

of $C_q(\Delta_q \times I)$ is a cycle. Since $\Delta_q \times I$ is homeomorphic to a starlike subspace of a Euclidean space, the sequence

$$C_{q+1}(\Delta_q + I) \xrightarrow{\ \partial\ } C_q(\Delta_q \times I) \xrightarrow{\ \partial\ } C_{q-1}(\Delta_q \times I)$$

is exact according to Exercise 3A. Hence there exists an element e_q

of $C_{q+1}(\Delta_q \times I)$ satisfying

$$\partial(e_q) = [C_q(\kappa_1)](\iota_q) - [C_q(\kappa_0)](\iota_q) - D_{q-1}[\partial(\iota_q)].$$

Having selected $e_q \in C_{q+1}(\Delta_q \times I)$, we define for any topological space X a function

$$F_q: S_q(X) \to C_{q+1}(X \times I)$$

as follows. Let $\xi \in S_q(X)$ be arbitrarily given. Then ξ is a map

$$\xi: \Delta_q \to X.$$

Consider the topological product

$$\xi \times i: \Delta_q \times I \to X \times I$$

and ξ and the identity map $i: I \to I$. Then we define F_q by taking

$$F_q(\xi) = [C_{q+1}(\xi \times i)](e_q).$$

Since $C_q(X)$ is the free Abelian group generated by $S_q(X)$, this function F_q extends to a unique homomorphism

$$D_q: C_q(X) \to C_{q+1}(X \times I).$$

The verification of the conditions (a) through (c) is straightforward and hence is omitted. This completes the inductive construction and proves (4.1). ‖

Because of conditions (a) and (b), the sequence $\{D_n | n \in Z\}$ is called a *chain homotopy* between the chain homomorphisms

$$C(\kappa_0), C(\kappa_1): [C(X), C(A)] \to [C(X \times I), C(A \times I)].$$

Because of condition (c), this chain homotopy is said to be *natural* or *functorial*.

The method used in the proof of (4.1) is a special case of the *general method of acyclic models*, [Sp, p. 164]. Instead of formulating its abstract general form, we prefer repeating the method in different forms for various special cases.

Now let us prove that

$$\kappa_0^* = \kappa_1^*: H^q(X \times I, A \times I; G) \to H^q(X, A; G).$$

For this purpose, let α denote an arbitrary element of $H^q(X \times I, A \times I; G)$. Select any cocycle $\phi \in Z^q(X \times I, A \times I; G)$ which represents α. Then, by definition, ϕ is a homomorphism

$$\phi: C_q(X \times I) \to G$$

satisfying $\phi \circ \partial = 0$ and $\phi[C_q(A \times I)] = 0$. Then $\kappa_0^*(\alpha)$ and $\kappa_1^*(\alpha)$ are represented by the cocycles

$$\phi \circ C_q(\kappa_0), \phi \circ C_q(\kappa_1): C_q(X) \to G,$$

respectively. The composition

$$\psi = \phi \circ D_{q-1}: C_{q-1}(X) \to G$$

of the homomorphism $D_{q-1}: C_{q-1}(X) \to C_q(X \times I)$ in (4.1) and $\phi: C_q(X \times I) \to G$ is a singular $(q-1)$-cochain of X over G. Since D_{q-1} sends $C_{q-1}(A)$ into $C_q(A \times I)$ and ϕ sends $C_q(A \times I)$ into 0, we have $\psi[C_{q-1}(A)] = 0$ and hence

$$\psi \in C^{q-1}(X, A; G).$$

By the definition of coboundary, we have

$$\delta\psi = \psi \circ \partial = \phi \circ D_{q-1} \circ \partial.$$

By condition (a) in (4.1), we have

$$D_{q-1} \circ \partial = C_q(\kappa_1) - C_q(\kappa_0) - \partial \circ D_q.$$

Consequently, we have

$$\delta\psi = \phi \circ C_q(\kappa_1) - \phi \circ C_q(\kappa_0)$$

because of $\phi \circ \partial = 0$. This implies $\kappa_0^*(\alpha) = \kappa_1^*(\alpha)$ and completes the verification of the homotopy axiom (V).

Next let us verify the excision axiom (VI). For this purpose, let us first construct, for every arbitrarily given topological space X and every integer n, two special homomorphisms

$$sd_n: C_n(X) \to C_n(X),$$
$$D_n: C_n(X) \to C_{n+1}(X)$$

satisfying the following three conditions:

(a) *For every integer n and every element c of $C_n(X)$, we have*

$$\partial[sd_n(c)] = sd_{n-1}[\partial(c)],$$
$$\partial[D_n(c)] + D_{n-1}[\partial(c)] = sd_n(c) - c.$$

(b) *For every subspace A of X, we have*

$$sd_n[C_n(A)] \subset C_n(A),$$

$$D_n[C_n(A)] \subset C_{n+1}(A).$$

(c) *For every map $f: X \to Y$ and every integer n, the following two rectangles are commutative:*

$$
\begin{array}{ccc}
C_n(X) & \xrightarrow{\ sd_n\ } & C_n(X) \\
\downarrow{\scriptstyle C_n(f)} & & \downarrow{\scriptstyle C_n(f)} \\
C_n(Y) & \xrightarrow{\ sd_n\ } & C_n(Y)
\end{array}
\qquad
\begin{array}{ccc}
C_n(X) & \xrightarrow{\ D_n\ } & C_{n+1}(X) \\
\downarrow{\scriptstyle C_n(f)} & & \downarrow{\scriptstyle C_{n+1}(f)} \\
C_n(Y) & \xrightarrow{\ D_n\ } & C_{n+1}(Y)
\end{array}
$$

First consider all $n < 0$. Since $C_n(X) = 0$ for every topological space X, we must have

$$sd_n = 0, \qquad D_n = 0.$$

Conditions (a) through (c) are obviously satisfied for every $n < 0$.

Next consider $n = 0$. For every topological space X, we define the homomorphisms sd_0 and D_0 by taking

$$sd_0(c) = c, \qquad D_0(c) = 0$$

for every element c of $C_0(X)$. Conditions (a) through (c) are obviously satisfied for every $n \leq 0$.

Next let $q \geq 0$ and consider the unit q-simplex Δ_q in the $(q + 1)$-dimensional Euclidean space R^{q+1}. Then Δ_q is a compact metric space and is a convex subspace of R^{q+1}.

A singular simplex $\xi: \Delta_n \to \Delta_q$ in Δ_q is said to be *linear* iff, for every-point $x = (x_0, x_1, \ldots, x_n)$ of Δ_n, we have

$$\xi(x) = \sum_{i=0}^{n} x_i \xi(v_i),$$

where v_i denotes the ith vertex of Δ_n as defined in Sec. 2.1. For each n, the linear singular n-simplexes in Δ_q generate a direct summand $L_n(\Delta_q)$ of the free Abelian group $C_n(\Delta_q)$. Obviously we have

$$L_n(\Delta_0) = C_n(\Delta_0),$$

$$\partial[L_n(\Delta_q)] \subset L_{n-1}(\Delta_q).$$

A linear singular simplex $\xi: \Delta_n \to \Delta_q$ is completely determined by the $n + 1$ points $\xi(v_0), \xi(v_1), \ldots, \xi(v_n)$ in Δ_q. For any $n + 1$ points $w_0, w_1, \ldots,$

w_n in Δ_q, we shall use $(w_0, w_1, \ldots, w_n)$ to denote the linear singular simplex $\xi: \Delta_n \rightarrow \Delta_q$ satisfying

$$\xi(v_i) = w_i \qquad (i = 0, 1, \ldots, n).$$

Then we clearly have

$$\partial(w_0, w_1, \ldots, w_n) = \sum_{i=0}^{n} (-1)^i (w_0, \ldots, \hat{w}_i, \ldots, w_n),$$

where the circumflex over $\hat{w}_i$ means that w_i is omitted.

Since $L_n(\Delta_q)$ is the free Abelian group generated by the linear singular n-simplexes in Δ_q, we may define a homomorphism

$$h_n: L_n(\Delta_q) \rightarrow L_{n+1}(\Delta_q)$$

by taking

$$h_n(w_0, w_1, \ldots, w_n) = (c, w_0, w_1, \ldots, w_n)$$

for every linear singular n-simplex $(w_0, w_1, \ldots, w_n)$ in Δ_q, where c denotes the centroid of Δ_q; that is, $c = (c_0, c_1, \ldots, c_q)$ with

$$c_i = \frac{1}{q+1} \qquad (i = 0, 1, \ldots, q).$$

Now let us complete the construction by induction on n. For this purpose, let q denote any positive integer and assume that sd_n and D_n have been constructed satisfying the conditions (a) through (c) and the following condition:

(d)   For every integer $m \geq 0$, we have

$$sd_n[L_n(\Delta_m)] \subset L_n(\Delta_m),$$
$$D_n[L_n(\Delta_m)] \subset L_{n+1}(\Delta_m)$$

for every $n < q$.

Note that (d) is obviously satisfied when $q = 1$.

Consider the identity map $\iota_q: \Delta_q \rightarrow \Delta_q$ as a linear singular q-simplex in Δ_q. By means of the homomorphisms h_n and condition (d), we define

$$e_q = h_{q-1}[sd_{q-1}(\partial \iota_q)] \in L_q(\Delta_q),$$
$$k_q = h_q[e_q - \iota_q - D_{q-1}(\partial \iota_q)] \in L_{q+1}(\Delta_q).$$

To define sd_q and D_q, let X denote an arbitrary topological space. Let

$$\xi: \Delta_q \rightarrow X$$

be an arbitrary singular q-simplex in X. As a continuous map, ξ induces a homomorphism

$$C_n(\xi): C_n(\Delta_q) \to C_n(X)$$

for every integer n. Since $C_q(X)$ is the free Abelian group generated by the singular q-simplexes in X, we can define the homomorphisms sd_q and D_q by taking

$$sd_q(\xi) = [C_q(\xi)](e_q),$$
$$D_q(\xi) = [C_{q+1}(\xi)](k_q)$$

for every singular q-simplex ξ in X. The verification of conditions (a) through (d) is straightforward and hence is omitted. This completes the construction of the homomorphisms sd_n and D_n.

Because of conditions (a) and (b), the sequence $sd = \{sd_n | n \in Z\}$ is a chain homomorphism

$$sd: [C(X), C(A)] \to [C(X), C(A)]$$

and the sequence $D = \{D_n | n \in Z\}$ is a chain homotopy between sd and the identity chain homomorphism

$$id: [C(X), C(A)] \to [C(X), C(A)].$$

Because of condition (c), sd and D are said to be *natural* or *functorial*.

For every integer $m \geqslant 0$, we define a chain homomorphism

$$sd^m: [C(X), C(A)] \to [C(X), C(A)]$$

inductively by taking $sd^0 = id$ and

$$sd^m = sd \circ sd^{m-1}$$

for every $m > 0$.

Now let us consider a collection

$$\gamma = \{E_\mu | \mu \in M\}$$

of subsets of a topological space X such that

$$X = \bigcup_{\mu \in M} \mathrm{Int}(E_\mu).$$

A singular simplex $\xi: \Delta_n \to X$ is said to be *small* (with respect to γ) iff there exists a $\mu \in M$ with $\xi(\Delta_n) \subset E_\mu$. The small singular n-simplexes in X generate a direct summand $K_n(X)$ of the free Abelian group $C_n(X)$. Obviously we have

$$\partial[K_n(X)] \subset K_{n-1}(X).$$

Thus we obtain a semiexact lower sequence

$$\cdots \to K_{n+1}(X) \xrightarrow{\ \partial\ } K_n(X) \xrightarrow{\ \partial\ } K_{n-1}(X) \to \cdots$$

which will be referred to as the *small subcomplex* $K(X)$ of the integral singular chain complex $C(X)$ with respect to γ.

For an arbitrarily given subspace A of X, let

$$K(A) = K(X) \cap C(A).$$

Then $K(A)$ is a subcomplex of $K(X)$. Let us consider the inclusion chain homomorphism

$$\theta \colon [K(X), K(A)] \to [C(X), C(A)].$$

Lemma 4.2. *The inclusion chain homomorphism θ is a chain equivalence; in other words, there exists a chain homomorphism*

$$\tau \colon [C(X), C(A)] \to [K(X), K(A)]$$

such that the composed chain homomorphisms $\theta \circ \tau$ and $\tau \circ \theta$ are chain homotopic to the identity chain homomorphisms in the sense of [H6, Chap. I, Sec. 6].

Proof. Consider an arbitrarily given singular simplex $\xi \colon \Delta_n \to X$. For each $\mu \in M$, let

$$U_\mu = \xi^{-1}[\mathrm{Int}(E_\mu)].$$

Then $\beta = \{U_\mu | \mu \in M\}$ is an open cover of the compact metric space Δ_n. Let $\lambda > 0$ denote the *Lebesgue number* of β as defined in [H7, p. 123].

For every singular n-chain

$$c = \sum_\sigma a_\sigma \sigma \in C_n(\Delta_n),$$

we define

$$\mathrm{mesh}(c) = \sup\{\mathrm{diam}\ \sigma(\Delta_n) | a_\sigma \neq 0\}.$$

If c is linear, then one can easily verify

$$\mathrm{mesh}[sd(c)] \leqslant \left(\frac{n}{n+1}\right) \mathrm{mesh}(c).$$

Let $k(\xi)$ denote the smallest nonnegative integer satisfying

$$\left(\frac{n}{n+1}\right)^{k(\xi)} \mathrm{diam}(\Delta_n) \leqslant \lambda.$$

Let $\iota_n \colon \Delta_n \to \Delta_n$ denote the identity map. Then ι_n is a linear singular

n-simplex in Δ_n with

$$\text{mesh}[sd^{k(\xi)}(\iota_n)] \leqslant \lambda.$$

Since $sd^{k(\xi)}(\xi)$ is the image of $sd^{k(\xi)}(\iota_n)$ under the homomorphism $C_n(\xi)$, this implies

$$sd^{k(\xi)}(\xi) \in K_n(X).$$

It is clear that $k(\xi) = 0$ iff ξ is small and that

$$k[\xi^{(i)}] \leqslant k(\xi)$$

holds for every integer $i = 0, 1, \ldots, n$, where $\xi^{(i)}$ denotes the ith face of ξ.

For every integer n, define a homomorphism

$$\Omega_n : C_n(X) \to C_{n+1}(X)$$

as follows. If $n < 0$, let Ω_n denote the trivial homomorphism. For $n \geqslant 0$, we define Ω_n by taking

$$\Omega_n(\xi) = \sum_{j=0}^{k(\xi)-1} D_n[sd^j(\xi)]$$

for every singular n-simplex ξ in X, where D_n stands for the homomorphism constructed above. Then we have $\Omega_n(\xi) = 0$ iff ξ is small. Since

$$\partial[\Omega_n(\xi)] = \sum_{j=0}^{k(\xi)-1} \{ sd^{j+1}(\xi) - sd^j(\xi) - D_{n-1}[sd^j(\partial\xi)] \}$$

$$= sd^{k(\xi)}(\xi) - \xi - \sum_{j=0}^{k(\xi)-1} \left\{ \sum_{i=0}^{n} (-1)^i D_{n-1}[sd^j(\xi^{(i)})] \right\},$$

$$\Omega_{n-1}(\partial\xi) = \sum_{i=0}^{n} (-1)^i \left\{ \sum_{j=0}^{k(\xi^{(i)})-1} D_{n-1}[sd^j(\xi^{(i)})] \right\},$$

the singular n-chain

$$\tau(\xi) = \xi + \partial[\Omega_n(\xi)] + \Omega_{n-1}[\partial(\xi)]$$

$$= \sum_{i=0}^{n} (-1)^i \left\{ \sum_{j=k(\xi^{(i)})}^{k(\xi)-1} D_{n-1}[sd^j(\xi^{(i)})] \right\}$$

is in the subgroup $K_n(X)$ of $C_n(X)$.

Since $C_n(X)$ is the free Abelian group generated by all singular n-simplexes in X, the assignment $\xi \to \tau(\xi)$ defines a unique homomorphism

$$\tau_n : C_n(X) \to K_n(X).$$

One can easily verify that τ_n sends $C_n(A)$ into $K_n(A)$ and commutes with the boundary operator ∂. Hence we obtain a chain homomorphism

$$\tau: [C(X), C(A)] \to [K(X), K(A)].$$

It remains to prove that $\theta \circ \tau$ and $\tau \circ \theta$ are chain homotopic to the identity chain homomorphisms.

For this purpose, let us first consider

$$\theta \circ \tau: [C(X), C(A)] \to [C(X), C(A)].$$

Let $\xi: \Delta_n \to X$ be an arbitrary singular simplex in X. Then we have

$$(\theta \circ \tau)(\xi) - \xi = \tau(\xi) - \xi = \partial[\Omega_n(\xi)] + \Omega_{n-1}[\partial(\xi)].$$

This implies that the sequence

$$\Omega = \{\Omega_n | n \in Z\}$$

is a chain homotopy between $\theta \circ \tau$ and the identity chain homomorphism.

Next let us consider

$$\tau \circ \theta: [K(X), K(A)] \to [K(X), K(A)].$$

Let $\xi: \Delta_n \to X$ denote any small singular simplex in X. Then we have

$$\Omega_n(\xi) = 0, \qquad \Omega_{n-1}[\partial(\xi)] = 0.$$

Consequently, we obtain

$$(\tau \circ \theta)(\xi) = \tau(\xi) = \xi.$$

This proves that $\tau \circ \theta$ is the identity chain homomorphism and completes the proof of (4.2). ‖

To verify the excision axiom (VI), let (X, A) denote any topological pair and consider an arbitrary open subset U of X satisfying

$$\text{Cl}(U) \subset \text{Int}(A).$$

Then we have

$$\text{Int}(A) \cup \text{Int}(X \setminus U) = X.$$

Hence we may apply (4.3) to the special case where

$$\gamma = \{A, X \setminus U\}.$$

Therefore the inclusion chain homomorphism

$$\theta: [K(X), K(A)] \to [C(X), C(A)]$$

is a chain equivalence. Furthermore, we also have

$$C(X \setminus U) \subset K(X),$$

$$C(A \setminus U) \subset K(A) = C(A).$$

This gives us an inclusion chain homomorphism

$$\rho: [C(X \setminus U), C(A \setminus U)] \to [K(X), K(A)].$$

The composition $\theta \circ \rho$ is the inclusion chain homomorphism

$$C(e): [C(X \setminus U), C(A \setminus U)] \to [C(X), C(A)]$$

induced by the inclusion map

$$e: (X \setminus U, A \setminus U) \to (X, A).$$

For every integer n, consider the subgroup

$$C^n[K(X), K(A); G] = \{\phi \in \mathrm{Hom}[K_n(X), G] \mid \phi [K_n(A)] = 0\}$$

of the Abelian group $\mathrm{Hom}[K_n(X), G]$ of all homomorphisms from $K_n(X)$ to G. This gives rise to a cochain complex

$$\cdots \to C^{n-1}[K(X), K(A); G] \xrightarrow{\delta} C^n[K(X), K(A); G] \xrightarrow{\delta} C^{n+1}[K(X), K(A); G] \to \cdots.$$

In the group $C^n[K(X), K(A); G]$, let

$$Z^n[K(X), K(A); G] = \mathrm{Ker}(\delta),$$

$$B^n[K(X), K(A); G] = \mathrm{Im}(\delta).$$

The quotient group

$$H^n[K(X), K(A); G] = Z^n[K(X), K(A); G]/B^n[K(X), K(A); G]$$

is called the *n-dimensional cohomology group of* $[K(X), K(A)]$ *over* G.

For every integer n, the chain homomorphisms ρ and θ induce homomorphisms

$$\rho^*: H^n[K(X), K(A); G] \to H^n(X \setminus U, A \setminus U; G).$$

$$\theta^*: H^n(X, A; G) \to H^n[K(X), K(A); G].$$

Their composition $\rho^* \circ \theta^*$ is the induced homomorphism

$$e^*: H^n(X, A; G) \to H^n(X \setminus U, A \setminus U; G).$$

Since θ is a chain equivalence, one can easily show that θ^* is an isomorphism. On the other hand, since ρ induces an isomorphism

$$C^n(\rho; G): C^n[K(X), K(A); G] \approx C^n(X \backslash U, A \backslash U; G)$$

for every n, then ρ^* is also an isomorphism. Consequently, we obtain

$$e^* = \rho^* \circ \theta^*: H^n(X, A; G) \approx H^n(X \backslash U, A \backslash U; G).$$

This completes the verification of the excision axiom (VI).

Finally, the dimension axiom (VII) is satisfied because of Exercise 2A. Consequently, $\mathscr{H}$ is a cohomology theory on the admissible category $\mathscr{C}_T$ of all topological pairs (X, A) and all maps of such pairs. By Exercise 2A, the coefficient group of $\mathscr{H}$ is isomorphic to a given Abelian group G. This proves the following theorem.

Theorem 4.3. (*Existence Theorem*). *For every admissible category $\mathscr{C}$ and every Abelian group G, there exists a cohomology theory $\mathscr{H}$ defined on $\mathscr{C}$ and with coefficient group isomorphic to G.*

EXERCISES
4A. By means of (4.1), verify the homotopy axiom for singular homology theory.
4B. By means of (4.2), verify the excision axiom for singular homology theory.

Chapter 3

ALEXANDER COHOMOLOGY THEORY

In the present chapter, we shall give a leisurely detailed exposition of the Alexander cohomology theory, which has no obvious corresponding homology theory. This cohomology theory was accurately called SWAK cohomology theory by the topology school of A. D. Wallace, because it was first introduced by Alexander and Kolmogoroff independently and was later improved by Spanier at the suggestion of Wallace. The reason for its inclusion in the present text is that it is used in the Alexander duality theorem, which will be established in Chapter 5.

1. Cochain Complex of Functions

Consider an arbitrary nonempty topological space X and any given additive Abelian group G. For every integer $n \geq 0$, let

$$F^n(X; G)$$

denote the set of all functions

$$\phi: X^{n+1} \to G$$

from the Cartesian power X^{n+1} of X into G. Then $F^n(X; G)$ forms an Abelian group under the *functional addition*; that is, for any two elements ξ and η in $F^n(X; G)$, $\xi + \eta$ is the element of $F^n(X; G)$ defined by

$$(\xi + \eta)(x) = \xi(x) + \eta(x)$$

for every element $x = (x_0, x_1, \ldots, x_n)$ of X^{n+1}. For completeness, we also define $F^n(X; G) = 0$ for every negative integer n and $F^n(\square; G) = 0$ for every integer n. Hence the additive Abelian group $F^n(X; G)$ is defined for every topological space, every additive group G, and every integer n.

For every integer n, let us define a homomorphism

$$\delta: F^n(X; G) \to F^{n+1}(X; G)$$

as follows. For every $n < 0$, let $\delta = 0$. Now assume $n \geqslant 0$. For every $\phi \in F^n(X; G)$, let $\delta(\phi)$ denote the element of $F^{n+1}(X; G)$ defined by

$$[\delta(\phi)](x) = \sum_{i=0}^{n+1} (-1)^i \phi(x_0, \ldots, \hat{x}_i, \ldots, x_{n+1})$$

for every element $x = (x_0, \ldots, x_{n+1})$ of X^{n+2}, where the circumflex over $\hat{x}_i$ means that x_i is omitted. The assignment $\phi \to \delta(\phi)$ defines a function

$$\delta: F^n(X; G) \to F^{n+1}(X; G)$$

which is obviously a homomorphism.

Lemma 1.1. *For every integer n, the composed homomorphism*

$$\delta^2 = \delta \circ \delta: F^{n-1}(X; G) \to F^{n+1}(X; G)$$

of the homomorphisms

$$F^{n-1}(X; G) \xrightarrow{\ \delta\ } F^n(X; G) \xrightarrow{\ \delta\ } F^{n+1}(X; G)$$

is a trivial homomorphism; that is, $\delta^2 = 0$.

Proof. The lemma is trivial for $n \leqslant 0$ since $F^{n-1}(X; G) = 0$. Assume $n > 0$. Let $\phi \in F^{n-1}(X; G)$ be arbitrarily given. It suffices to prove that $\delta[\delta(\phi)] = 0$.

For this purpose, let $x = (x_0, x_1, \ldots, x_{n+1})$ denote an arbitrary element of X^{n+2}. Then we have

$$\delta[\delta(\phi)](x) = \sum_{i=0}^{n+1} (-1)^i [\delta(\phi)](x_0, \ldots, \hat{x}_i, \ldots, x_{n+1})$$

$$= \sum_{i=0}^{n+1} (-1)^i \sum_{j=0}^{i-1} (-1)^j \phi(x_0, \ldots, \hat{x}_j, \ldots, \hat{x}_i, \ldots, x_{n+1})$$

$$+ \sum_{i=0}^{n+1} (-1)^i \sum_{j=i+1}^{n+1} (-1)^{j-1} \phi(x_0, \ldots, \hat{x}_i, \ldots, \hat{x}_j, \ldots, x_{n+1}).$$

Since these two terms cancel each other, we obtain

$$\delta[\delta(\phi)](x) = 0.$$

Since this is true for every $x \in X^{n+2}$, we have

$$\delta[\delta(\phi)] = 0.$$

This completes the proof of (1.1). ‖

Thus we obtain a cochain complex

$$\cdots \to F^{n-1}(X; G) \xrightarrow{\ \delta\ } F^{n}(X; G) \xrightarrow{\ \delta\ } F^{n+1}(X; G) \to \cdots$$

which will be denoted by $F^*(X; G)$ and will be referred to as the *cochain complex of functions* for X over G.

The cohomology groups of the cochain complex $F^*(X; G)$ can be defined in the usual way as follows.

For every integer n, let $Z_F^n(X; G)$ denote the kernel of the homomorphism

$$\delta\colon F^n(X; G) \to F^{n+1}(X; G)$$

and let $B_F^n(X; G)$ denote the image of the homomorphism

$$\delta\colon F^{n-1}(X; G) \to F^n(X; G).$$

Because of (1.1), we have

$$B_F^n(X; G) \subset Z_F^n(X; G).$$

The quotient group

$$H_F^n(X; G) = Z_F^n(X; G)/B_F^n(X; G)$$

is the *n-dimensional cohomology group* of the cochain complex $F^*(X; G)$.

Proposition 1.2. *If the topological space X is empty, then we have*

$$H_F^n(X; G) = 0$$

for every Abelian group G and every integer n.

Proof. By definition, we have $F^n(X; G) = 0$. Since $H_F^n(X; G)$ is a quotient group of a subgroup of $F^n(X; G)$, this implies that $H_F^n(X; G) = 0$. ‖

Proposition 1.3. *If the topological space X is nonempty, then we have*

$$H_F^n(X; G) \approx \begin{cases} G & (\text{if } n = 0), \\ 0 & (\text{if } n \neq 0). \end{cases}$$

Proof. For $n < 0$, we have $F^n(X; G) = 0$ by definition. As a quotient group of a subgroup of $F^n(X; G)$, we have $H_F^n(X; G) = 0$.

Next let us consider the case $n = 0$. Let ϕ denote an arbitrary element of $F^0(X; G)$. By definition, ϕ is a function $\phi: X \to G$. By the definition of δ, ϕ is in $Z_F^0(X; G)$ iff

$$\phi(x_1) - \phi(x_0) = [\delta(\phi)](x_0, x_1) = 0$$

for any two points x_0 and x_1 in X. This implies that $Z_F^0(X; G)$ consists of all constant functions from X into G. Hence we obtain

$$Z_F^0(X; G) \approx G.$$

On the other hand, we have

$$B_F^0(X; G) = \delta[F^{-1}(X; G)] = 0$$

since $F^{-1}(X; G) = 0$. This proves that

$$H_F^0(X; G) \approx G.$$

Throughout the remainder of the proof, we assume $n > 0$. It remains to prove that

$$B_F^n(X; G) = Z_F^n(X; G).$$

For this purpose, let $\phi: X^{n+1} \to G$ denote an arbitrary element in $Z_F^n(X; G)$. Select a fixed point x_* in X and define a function $\psi: X^n \to G$ by taking

$$\psi(x_0, x_1, \ldots, x_{n-1}) = \phi(x_*, x_0, x_1, \ldots, x_{n-1})$$

for every $(x_0, x_1, \ldots, x_{n-1}) \in X^n$. It suffices to prove that

$$\delta(\psi) = \phi.$$

For this purpose, let $x = (x_0, x_1, \ldots, x_n)$ denote an arbitrary element in X^{n+1}. Since $\phi \in Z_F^n(X; G)$, we have

$$[\delta(\phi)](x_*, x_0, x_1, \ldots, x_n) = 0.$$

Because of this, we obtain

$$[\delta(\psi)](x) = \sum_{i=1}^{n} (-1)^i \psi(x_0, x_1, \ldots, \hat{x}_i, \ldots, x_n)$$

$$= \sum_{i=1}^{n} (-1)^i \phi(x_*, x_0, x_1, \ldots, \hat{x}_i, \ldots, x_n)$$

$$= \phi(x).$$

This implies that $\delta(\psi) = \phi$ and completes the proof of (1.3). ‖

By (1.2) and (1.3), we see that the cohomology groups $H_F^n(X; G)$ are good only to determine whether or not X is empty. Since the topology of X is not used in the construction of these groups $H_F^n(X; G)$, certainly one should not expect much information about the topological space X from these groups.

EXERCISES

1A. Let (X, a) denote a nonempty topological space X and a given *base point* a in X. For every integer n and every Abelian group G, define a homomorphism

$$\partial: F^n(X; G) \to F^{n-1}(X; G)$$

as follows: If $n \leq 0$, let $\partial = 0$. In the case $n > 0$, define ∂ by taking

$$[\partial(\phi)](x) = \phi(a, x_1, \ldots, x_n) + \sum_{i=1}^{n} (-1)^i \phi(x_1, \ldots, x_i, a, x_{i+1}, \ldots, x_n)$$

for every $x = (x_1, \ldots, x_n) \in X^n$. Prove that

$$\partial^2 = \partial \circ \partial = 0.$$

Thus we obtain a chain complex

$$\cdots \to F^{n+1}(X; G) \xrightarrow{\partial} F^n(X; G) \xrightarrow{\partial} F^{n-1}(X; G) \to \cdots$$

which will be denoted by $F(X, a; G)$.

1B. Determine the homology groups of the chain complex $F(X, a; G)$.

2. Absolute Cohomology Groups

For an arbitrary nonempty topological space X and any Abelian group G, let us consider the cochain complex $F^*(X; G)$ of functions constructed in the preceding section. We shall use the topology of X to construct a more interesting quotient complex of $F^*(X; G)$.

Assume $n \geq 0$. A function

$$\phi: X^{n+1} \to G$$

is said to be *locally zero at a point* x of X iff there exists a neighborhood U of x in X such that

$$\phi(x_0, x_1, \ldots, x_n) = 0$$

whenever $x_i \in U$ holds for every $i = 0, 1, \ldots, n$.

By the *support* of an arbitrarily given function

$$\phi: X^{n+1} \to G,$$

we mean the subset $S(\phi)$ of X which is defined as follows. A point x of X

is in $S(\phi)$ iff ϕ is not locally zero at x. Consequently, $X \setminus S(\phi)$ consists of all points of X at which ϕ is locally zero.

Proposition 2.1. *The support $S(\phi)$ of any function $\phi: X^{n+1} \to G$ is a closed subset of the topological space X.*

Proof. It suffices to prove that $X \setminus S(\phi)$ is an open subset of X. For this purpose, let p denote any point in $X \setminus S(\phi)$. By definition, ϕ is locally zero at p. Hence there exists an open neighborhood U of p such that

$$\phi(x_0, x_1, \ldots, x_n) = 0$$

whenever $x_i \in U$ holds for every $i = 0, 1, \ldots, n$. Let q denote an arbitrary point in U. Since U is a neighborhood of q, it follows that ϕ is locally zero at q. This implies that U is contained in $X \setminus S(\phi)$ and hence $X \setminus S(\phi)$ is an open subset of X. ‖

A function $\phi: X^{n+1} \to G$ is said to be *locally zero* iff it is locally zero at every point of X. The following proposition is obvious.

Proposition 2.2. *A function $\phi: X^{n+1} \to G$ is locally zero iff*

$$S(\phi) = \square.$$

For the special case $n = 0$, we have the following proposition.

Proposition 2.3. *A function $\phi: X \to G$ is locally zero iff $\phi = 0$.*

Proof. The sufficiency is obvious. To prove the necessity, assume that ϕ is locally zero and let x denote an arbitrary point of X. By definition, there exists a neighborhood U of x in X such that $\phi(x_0) = 0$ for every point $x_0 \in U$. In particular, we have $\phi(x) = 0$. Since x is an arbitrary point of X, this proves that $\phi = 0$. ‖

For every integer $n \geqslant 0$, let

$$F_0^n(X; G)$$

denote the set of all functions $\phi: X^{n+1} \to G$ which are locally zero. For completeness, we also define

$$F_0^n(X; G) = 0 \qquad (n < 0).$$

Lemma 2.4. *For every integer n, $F_0^n(X; G)$ is a subgroup of the Abelian group $F^n(X; G)$.*

Proof. $F_0^n(X; G)$ is obviously a subset of $F^n(X; G)$. To prove that $F_0^n(X; G)$ is a subgroup of $F^n(X; G)$, let ϕ and ψ denote any two elements of $F_0^n(X; G)$ and consider an arbitrary point x of X. Since ϕ and ψ are

are locally zero, there exist neighborhoods U and V such that

$$\phi(y_0, y_1, \ldots, y_n) = 0, \qquad \psi(z_0, z_1, \ldots, z_n) = 0$$

whenever $y_i \in U$ and $z_i \in V$ hold for every $i = 0, 1, \ldots, n$. Let

$$W = U \cap V.$$

Then W is a neighborhood of x in X such that

$$(\phi - \psi)(x_0, x_1, \ldots, x_n) = \phi(x_0, x_1, \ldots, x_n) - \psi(x_0, x_1, \ldots, x_n) = 0$$

whenever $x_i \in W$ holds for every $i = 0, 1, \ldots, n$. This proves that $\phi - \psi \in F_0^n(X; G)$ and hence $F_0^n(X; G)$ is a subgroup of $F^n(X; G)$. $\|$

Lemma 2.5. *For every integer n, the homomorphism*

$$\delta: F^n(X; G) \to F^{n+1}(X; G)$$

sends $F_0^n(X; G)$ into $F_0^{n+1}(X; G)$.

Proof. If $n < 0$, the lemma is trivial because $F_0^n(X; G) = 0$. Assume $n \geqslant 0$ and let ϕ denote an arbitrary element of $F_0^n(X; G)$. To prove that $\delta(\phi) \in F_0^{n+1}(X; G)$, let x denote any point in X. Since ϕ is locally zero, there exists a neighborhood U of x in X such that

$$\phi(y_0, y_1, \ldots, y_n) = 0$$

whenever $y_i \in U$ holds for every $i = 0, 1, \ldots, n$. Consequently, we obtain

$$[\delta(\phi)](x_0, \ldots, x_{n+1}) = \sum_{i=0}^{n+1} (-1)^i \, \phi \, (x_0, \ldots, \hat{x}_i, \ldots, x_{n+1}) = 0$$

whenever $x_i \in U$ holds for every $i = 0, 1, \ldots, n+1$. This proves that $\delta(\phi) \in F_0^{n+1}(X; G)$ and completes the proof of (2.5). $\|$

For every integer n, the quotient group

$$C^n(X; G) = F^n(X; G)/F_0^n(X; G)$$

will be referred to as the *n-dimensional (Alexander) cochain group* of the space X over G. Its elements will be called the *n-dimensional (Alexander) cochains* of X over G.

Because of (2.5), the homomorphism $\delta: F^n(X; G) \to F^{n+1}(X; G)$ induces a homomorphism

$$\delta: C^n(X; G) \to C^{n+1}(X; G).$$

The following lemma is an immediate consequence of (1.1).

Lemma 2.6. *For every integer n, the composed homomorphism*

$$\delta^2 = \delta \circ \delta \colon C^{n-1}(X;G) \to C^{n+1}(X;G)$$

of the homomorphisms

$$C^{n-1}(X;G) \xrightarrow{\ \delta\ } C^n(X;G) \xrightarrow{\ \delta\ } C^{n+1}(X;G)$$

is a trivial homomorphism; that is, $\delta^2 = 0$.

Thus we obtain a cochain complex

$$\cdots \to C^{n-1}(X;G) \xrightarrow{\ \delta\ } C^n(X;G) \xrightarrow{\ \delta\ } C^{n+1}(X;G) \to \cdots$$

which will be denoted by $C^*(X;G)$ and will be referred to as the *Alexander cochain complex* of X over G. The homomorphisms δ in $C^*(X;G)$ will be called *coboundary operators*.

The cohomology groups of this cochain complex $C^*(X;G)$ can be defined in the usual way as follows.

For every integer n, let $Z^n(X;G)$ denote the kernel of the homomorphism

$$\delta \colon C^n(X;G) \to C^{n+1}(X;G)$$

and let $B^n(X;G)$ denote the image of the homomorphism

$$\delta \colon C^{n-1}(X;G) \to C^n(X;G).$$

The elements of $Z^n(X;G)$ will be called the *n-dimensional (Alexander) cocycles* of X over G and those of $B^n(X;G)$ will be called the *n-dimensional (Alexander) coboundaries* of X over G.

Because of (2.6), we have

$$B^n(X;G) \subset Z^n(X;G).$$

The quotient group

$$H^n(X;G) = Z^n(X;G)/B^n(X;G)$$

will be referred to as the *n-dimensional Alexander cohomology group of the topological space X over G*.

EXERCISES

2A. Let X denote a singleton space. Prove that

$$C^n(X;G) = F^n(X;G)$$

holds for every integer n. Hence deduce that

$$H^n(X;G) \approx \begin{cases} G & (\text{if } n = 0), \\ 0 & (\text{if } n \neq 0). \end{cases}$$

2B. By means of an example, show that the homomorphism

$$\partial: F^n(X; G) \to F^{n-1}(X; G)$$

may fail to send $F_0^n(X; G)$ into $F_0^{n-1}(X; G)$.

2C. Consider an arbitrarily given Abelian group G as a topological group with discrete topology. Prove that a function $\phi: X \to G$ is *locally constant* iff ϕ is continuous. Then deduce that $H^0(X; G)$ is isomorphic to the group of all continuous maps of X into G.

3. Relative Cohomology Groups

Consider an arbitrarily given map

$$f: X \to Y$$

from a topological space X into a topological space Y.

For every integer n, define a homomorphism

$$F^n(f; G): F^n(Y; G) \to F^n(X; G)$$

as follows. If $n < 0$, let $F^n(f; G) = 0$. Assume $n \geqslant 0$ and let ϕ denote an arbitrary element in $F^n(Y; G)$. Define an element $\psi \in F^n(X; G)$ by taking

$$\psi(x_0, x_1, \ldots, x_n) = \phi[f(x_0), f(x_1), \ldots, f(x_n)]$$

for every point $(x_0, x_1, \ldots, x_n)$ of X^{n+1}. The assignment $\phi \to \psi$ defines a function $F^n(f; G)$ which is clearly a homomorphism.

Lemma 3.1. *For every integer n, the homomorphism*

$$F^n(f; G): F^n(Y; G) \to F^n(X; G)$$

sends $F_0^n(Y; G)$ into $F_0^n(X; G)$.

Proof. Since the lemma is trivial when $n < 0$, we assume $n \geqslant 0$.

For convenience, let $h = F^n(f; G)$. Let ϕ denote an arbitrary element of $F_0^n(Y; G)$. To prove that $h(\phi) \in F_0^n(X; G)$, let x denote any point in the space X. Since ϕ is locally zero at the point $y = f(x)$ of the space Y, there exists a neighborhood V of y in Y such that

$$\phi(y_0, y_1, \ldots, y_n) = 0$$

whenever $y_i \in V$ holds for every $i = 0, 1, \ldots, n$. Since f is a map, the inverse image $U = f^{-1}(V)$ is a neighborhood of x in X. Since we have

$$[h(\phi)](x_0, x_1, \ldots, x_n) = \phi[f(x_0), f(x_1), \ldots, f(x_n)] = 0$$

whenever $x_i \in U$ holds for every $i = 0, 1, \cdots, n$, it follows that $h(\phi)$ is locally zero at x. Since x is any point of X, we have

$$h(\phi) \in F_0^n(X; G).$$

Since ϕ is any element of $F_0^n(Y; G)$, this completes the proof of (3.1). ‖
Because of (3.1), the homomorphism

$$F^n(f; G): F^n(Y; G) \to F^n(X; G)$$

induces a homomorphism

$$C^n(f; G): C^n(Y; G) \to C^n(X; G)$$

which will be referred to as the *induced homomorphism* of f on the n-dimensional Alexander cochain groups.

Lemma 3.2. *For every integer n, the following rectangle is commutative:*

$$
\begin{array}{ccc}
C^n(Y; G) & \xrightarrow{\delta} & C^{n+1}(Y; G) \\
\downarrow{\scriptstyle c^n(f;G)} & & \downarrow{\scriptstyle c^{n+1}(f;G)} \\
C^n(X; G) & \xrightarrow{\delta} & C^{n+1}(X; G)
\end{array}
$$

Proof. It follows from the definitions that the rectangle

$$
\begin{array}{ccc}
F^n(Y; G) & \xrightarrow{\delta} & F^{n+1}(Y; G) \\
\downarrow{\scriptstyle F^n(f;G)} & & \downarrow{\scriptstyle F^{n+1}(f;G)} \\
F^n(X; G) & \xrightarrow{\delta} & F^{n+1}(X; G)
\end{array}
$$

is commutative. By passing to the quotient groups, we immediately obtain (3.2). ‖

Now let us consider an arbitrary subspace A of any topological space X. Applying the preceding results to the inclusion map

$$i: A \to X,$$

we obtain a homomorphism

$$C^n(i; G): C^n(X; G) \to C^n(A; G)$$

for every integer n.

The kernel of the homomorphism $C^n(i; G)$ will be denoted by

$$C^n(X, A; G)$$

and will be called the *n-dimensional (Alexander) cochain group* of the topological pair (X, A) over G or of X modulo A over G. Obviously we have the following lemma.

Lemma 3.3. *For every integer n, we have*

$$C^n(X, \square; G) = C^n(X; G).$$

Next let us establish the following lemma.

Lemma 3.4. *For every integer n, the coboundary operator*

$$\delta: C^n(X; G) \to C^{n+1}(X; G)$$

sends the subgroup $C^n(X, A; G)$ of $C^n(X; G)$ into the subgroup $C^{n+1}(X, A; G)$ of $C^{n+1}(X; G)$.

Proof. By (3.2), the rectangle

$$
\begin{array}{ccc}
C^n(X; G) & \xrightarrow{\ \delta\ } & C^{n+1}(X; G) \\
\downarrow{\scriptstyle C^n(i;G)} & & \downarrow{\scriptstyle C^{n+1}(i;G)} \\
C^n(A; G) & \xrightarrow{\ \delta\ } & C^{n+1}(A; G)
\end{array}
$$

is commutative. For convenience, let

$$h = C^n(i; G), \qquad k = C^{n+1}(i; G).$$

To prove (3.4), let ϕ denote any element in $C^n(X, A; G)$. Then we have $h(\phi) = 0$, and hence

$$k[\delta(\phi)] = \delta[h(\phi)] = \delta(0) = 0.$$

This implies that $\delta(\phi) \in C^{n+1}(X, A; G)$ and proves (3.4). ∥

Because of (3.4), the homomorphism

$$\delta: C^n(X; G) \to C^{n+1}(X; G)$$

defines a homomorphism

$$\delta: C^n(X, A; G) \to C^{n+1}(X, A; G)$$

for every integer n. The following lemma is an immediate consequence of (2.6).

Lemma 3.5. *For every integer n, the composed homomorphism*

$$\delta^2 = \delta \circ \delta: C^{n-1}(X, A; G) \to C^{n+1}(X, A; G)$$

of the homomorphisms

$$C^{n-1}(X, A; G) \xrightarrow{\delta} C^n(X, A; G) \xrightarrow{\delta} C^{n+1}(X, A; G)$$

is a trivial homomorphism; that is, $\delta^2 = 0$.

Thus we obtain a cochain complex

$$\cdots \to C^{n-1}(X, A; G) \xrightarrow{\delta} C^n(X, A; G) \xrightarrow{\delta} C^{n+1}(X, A; G) \to \cdots$$

which will be denoted by $C^*(X, A; G)$ and will be referred to as the *Alexander cochain complex* of the topological pair (X, A) over G. The homomorphisms δ are called *coboundary operators*.

The cohomology groups of this cochain complex $C^*(X, A; G)$ can be defined in the usual way as follows.

For every integer n, let $Z^n(X, A; G)$ denote the kernel of the homomorphism

$$\delta \colon C^n(X, A; G) \to C^{n+1}(X, A; G)$$

and let $B^n(X, A; G)$ denote the image of the homomorphism

$$\delta \colon C^{n-1}(X, A; G) \to C^n(X, A; G).$$

The elements of $Z^n(X, A; G)$ will be called the *n-dimensional (Alexander) cocycles* of X modulo A over G, and those of $B^n(X, A; G)$ will be called the *n-dimensional (Alexander) coboundaries* of X modulo A over G.

Because of (3.5), we have

$$B^n(X, A; G) \subset Z^n(X, A; G).$$

The quotient group

$$H^n(X, A; G) = Z^n(X, A; G) / B^n(X, A; G)$$

will be referred to as the *n-dimensional Alexander cohomology group of the topological pair* (X, A) over G or of the topological space X modulo the subspace A over G.

The following propositions are obvious.

Proposition 3.6. *For every topological space X and every integer n, we have*

$$H^n(X, \square; G) = H^n(X; G).$$

Proposition 3.7. *For every topological space X and every integer n, we have*

$$H^n(X, X; G) = 0.$$

EXERCISES

3A. For every integer n, let $F^n(X, A; G)$ denote the inverse image of $F_0^n(A; G)$ under the induced homomorphism

$$F^n(i; G): F^n(X; G) \to F^n(A; G)$$

of the inclusion map $i: A \to X$. Prove that

$$C^n(X, A; G) \approx F^n(X, A; G)/F_0^n(X; G).$$

3B. Prove that for every integer n, the induced homomorphism

$$F^n(i; G): F^n(X; G) \to F^n(A; G)$$

of the inclusion map $i: A \to X$ is an endomorphism. Hence, deduce that the homomorphism

$$C^n(i; G): C^n(X; G) \to C^n(A; G)$$

is also an epimorphism.

3C. Prove that $H^0(X, A; G)$ is isomorphic to the group of all locally constant functions from X into G. Hence deduce that

$$H^0(X, A; G) = 0$$

if X is connected and $A \neq \square$.

4. Induced Homomorphisms

Consider an arbitrarily given map

$$f: (X, A) \to (Y, B)$$

from a topological pair (X, A) into a topological pair (Y, B). By definition, f is a map from X into Y satisfying

$$f(A) \subset B.$$

Lemma 4.1. *For every integer n, the induced homomorphism*

$$C^n(f; G): C^n(Y; G) \to C^n(X; G)$$

sends the subgroup $C^n(Y, B; G)$ of $C^n(Y; G)$ into the subgroup $C^n(X, A; G)$ of $C^n(X; G)$.

Proof. Consider the map $g: A \to B$ defined by f and the inclusion maps

$$i: A \to X, \qquad j: B \to Y.$$

It follows from the definition in the preceding section that the rectangle

$$C^n(Y; G) \xrightarrow{\;\;C^n(f;G)\;\;} C^n(X; G)$$

$$\downarrow {\scriptstyle C^n(j;G)} \qquad\qquad \downarrow {\scriptstyle C^n(i;G)}$$

$$C^n(B; G) \xrightarrow{\;\;C^n(g;G)\;\;} C^n(A; G)$$

is commutative. As in the proof of (3.4), this implies that $C^n(f; G)$ sends the kernel of $C^n(j; G)$ into the kernel of $C^n(i; G)$. This completes the proof of (4.1). ∥

Because of (4.1), the homomorphism $C^n(f; G)$ on $C^n(Y; G)$ defines a homomorphism

$$C^n(f; G): C^n(Y, B; G) \to C^n(X, A; G)$$

for every integer n. The following two lemmas are obvious.

Lemma 4.2. *For every integer n, the induced homomorphism*

$$C^n(i; G): C^n(X, A; G) \to C^n(X, A; G)$$

of the identity map $i: (X, A) \to (X, A)$ *is the identity automorphism of* $C^n(X, A; G)$.

Lemma 4.3. *For arbitrary maps*

$$f: (X, A) \to (Y, B), \qquad g: (Y, B) \to (Z, C),$$

the relation

$$C^n(g \circ f; G) = C^n(f; G) \circ C^n(g; G)$$

holds for every integer n.

The following lemma is an immediate consequence of (3.2) and (3.4).

Lemma 4.4. *For every integer n, the following rectangle is commutative:*

$$C^n(Y, B; G) \xrightarrow{\;\;\delta\;\;} C^{n+1}(Y, B; G)$$

$$\downarrow {\scriptstyle C^n(f;G)} \qquad\qquad \downarrow {\scriptstyle C^{n+1}(f;G)}$$

$$C^n(X, A; G) \xrightarrow{\;\;\delta\;\;} C^{n+1}(X, A; G)$$

Because of (4.4), the induced homomorphism

$$C^n(f; G): C^n(Y, B; G) \to C^n(X, A; G)$$

carries $Z^n(Y, B; G)$ into $Z^n(X, A; G)$ and $B^n(Y, B; G)$ into $B^n(X, A; G)$. Hence $C^n(f; G)$ induces a homomorphism

$$f^* = H^n(f; G): H^n(Y, B; G) \to H^n(X, A; G)$$

which will be referred to as the *induced homomorphism* of the given map

$$f: (X, A) \to (Y, B)$$

on the *n*-dimensional Alexander cohomology groups. The following two propositions are immediate consequences of (4.2) and (4.3).

Proposition 4.5. *For every integer n, the induced homomorphism*

$$H^n(i; G): H^n(X, A; G) \to H^n(X, A; G)$$

of the identity map $i: (X, A) \to (X, A)$ *is the identity automorphism of* $H^n(X, A; G)$.

Proposition 4.6. *For arbitrary maps*

$$f: (X, A) \to (Y, B), \qquad g: (Y, B) \to (Z, C),$$

the relation

$$H^n(g \circ f; G) = H^n(f; G) \circ H^n(g; G)$$

holds for every integer n.

EXERCISES

4A. Verify that the induced homomorphism

$$C^n(f; G): C^n(Y, B; G) \to C^n(X, A; G)$$

of any map $f: (X, A) \to (Y, B)$ carries $Z^n(Y, B; G)$ into $Z^n(X, A; G)$ and $B^n(Y, B; G)$ into $B^n(X, A; G)$.

4B. By means of an example, show that the induced homomorphism

$$C^n(i; G): C^n(X; G) \to C^n(A; G)$$

of an inclusion map $i: A \to X$ does necessarily send $Z^n(X; G)$ *onto* $Z^n(A; G)$, although it is an epimorphism according to Exercise 3B.

4C. Prove the following assertions for the induced homomorphism

$$f^*: H^0(Y; G) \to H^0(X; G)$$

of an arbitrarily given map $f: X \to Y$:
(a) f^* is a monomorphism if f is surjective.
(b) f^* is an epimorphism if X is connected.
(c) f^* is a monomorphism if Y is connected.

5. Coboundary Operators

Let (X, A) denote an arbitrarily given topological pair and consider the inclusion map

$$i: A \to X.$$

For every Abelian group G and every integer n, i induces a homomorphism

$$h^n = C^n(i; G): C^n(X; G) \to C^n(A; G).$$

By Exercise 3B, h^n is an epimorphism. According to the definition, $C^n(X, A; G)$ is the kernel of h^n.

Now let us construct a function

$$\gamma: Z^n(A; G) \to H^{n+1}(X, A; G)$$

for every integer n as follows. Let z denote an arbitrary element of $Z^n(A; G)$. Since h^n is an epimorphism, there is a cochain $u \in C^n(X; G)$ with $h^n(u) = z$. Consider the element

$$\delta(u) \in C^{n+1}(X; G),$$

where $\delta: C^n(X; G) \to C^{n+1}(X; G)$ denotes the coboundary operator on $C^n(X; G)$.

Lemma 5.1. *The element $\delta(u)$ is contained in the subgroup $C^{n+1}(X, A; G)$ of $C^{n+1}(X; G)$.*
Proof. According to (3.2), the rectangle

$$
\begin{array}{ccc}
C^n(X; G) & \xrightarrow{\delta} & C^{n+1}(X; G) \\
\downarrow{\scriptstyle h^n} & & \downarrow{\scriptstyle h^{n+1}} \\
C^n(A; G) & \xrightarrow{\delta} & C^{n+1}(A; G)
\end{array}
$$

is commutative. Since $\delta(x) = 0$, this implies that

$$h^{n+1}[\delta(u)] = \delta[h^n(u)] = \delta(x) = 0.$$

Hence $\delta(u) \in C^{n+1}(X, A; G)$. ||

Lemma 5.2. *The element* $\delta(u)$ *is contained in the subgroup* $Z^{n+1}(X, A; G)$ *of* $C^{n+1}(X, A; G)$.

Proof. Since the coboundary operator on $C^{n+1}(X, A; G)$ is the restriction of that on $C^{n+1}(X; G)$, we have

$$\delta[\delta(u)] = (\delta \circ \delta)(u) = 0.$$

Hence $\delta(u) \in Z^{n+1}(X, A; G)$. ||

Consider the natural projection

$$p: Z^{n+1}(X, A; G) \to H^{n+1}(X, A; G).$$

Lemma 5.3. *The element* $p[\delta(u)]$ *of* $H^{n+1}(X, A; G)$ *is independent of the choice of* $u \in C^n(X; G)$ *and hence depends only on the element* $z \in Z^n(A; G)$.

Proof. Let u and v denote any two elements of $C^n(X; G)$ satisfying

$$h^n(u) = z = h^n(v).$$

It suffices to prove that $p[\delta(u)] = p[\delta(v)]$.

For this purpose, let us consider the element $u - v$ of $C^n(X; G)$. Since

$$h^n(u - v) = h^n(u) - h^n(v) = z - z = 0,$$

it follows that $u - v$ is contained in the subgroup $C^n(X, A; G)$ of $C^n(X; G)$. This implies that the element $\delta(u - v)$ is contained in $B^{n+1}(X, A; G)$, and hence

$$p[\delta(u)] - p[\delta(v)] = p[\delta(u - v)] = 0.$$

This proves that $p[\delta(u)] = p[\delta(v)]$. ||

Because of (5.3), we may define the function

$$\gamma: Z^n(A; G) \to H^{n+1}(X, A; G)$$

by assigning to each element z of $Z^n(A; G)$ the element

$$\gamma(z) = p[\delta(u)] \in H^{n+1}(X, A; G)$$

with any $u \in C^n(X; G)$ satisfying $h^n(u) = z$.

Lemma 5.4. *This function* γ *is a homomorphism of* $Z^n(A; G)$ *into* $H^{n+1}(X, A; G)$.

Proof. Let y and z denote any two elements of $Z^n(A; G)$. Choose two elements u and v of $C^n(X; G)$ satisfying $h^n(u) = y$ and $h^n(v) = z$. By definition, we have

$$\gamma(y) = p[\delta(u)], \qquad \gamma(z) = p[\delta(v)].$$

Since $h^n(u + v) = y + z$, it follows that

$$\gamma(y + z) = p[\delta(u + v)] = p[\delta(u)] + p[\delta(v)] = \gamma(y) + \gamma(z).$$

Hence γ is a homomorphism. $\|$

Lemma 5.5.   *The kernel of this homomorphism γ contains the sub-group $B^n(A; G)$ of $Z^n(A; G)$.*

Proof.   Let z denote an arbitrary element of $B^n(A; G)$.   By the definition of $B^n(A; G)$, there exists an element y of $C^{n-1}(A; G)$ with $\delta(y) = z$. Since h^{n-1} sends $C^{n-1}(X; G)$ onto $C^{n-1}(A; G)$, there exists an element w of $C^{n-1}(X; G)$ satisfying $h^{n-1}(w) = y$.   Let $u = \delta(w)$.   Then we have

$$h^n(u) = h^n[\delta(w)] = \delta[h^{n-1}(w)] = \delta(y) = z.$$

According to the definition of γ, we have

$$\gamma(z) = p[\delta(u)] = p[\delta^2(w)] = p(0) = 0.$$

This completes the proof of (5.5). $\|$

Because of (5.5), the homomorphism

$$\gamma \colon Z^n(A; G) \to H^{n+1}(X, A; G)$$

induces a homomorphism

$$\delta \colon H^n(A; G) \to H^{n+1}(X, A; G)$$

which is called the *coboundary operator* for the topological pair (X, A) on the Alexander cohomology group $H^n(A; G)$.

Now let us consider an arbitrarily given map

$$f \colon (X, A) \to (Y, B)$$

of a topological pair (X, A) into a topological pair (Y, B).   Let

$$g \colon A \to B$$

denote the map defined by f.   Then we have the following proposition.

Proposition 5.6.   *For every integer n and every Abelian group G, the rectangle*

$$
\begin{array}{ccc}
H^n(B; G) & \xrightarrow{\ \delta\ } & H^{n+1}(Y, B; G) \\
\Big\downarrow{\scriptstyle g^*} & & \Big\downarrow{\scriptstyle f^*} \\
H^n(A; G) & \xrightarrow{\ \delta\ } & H^{n+1}(X, A; G)
\end{array}
$$

is commutative; that is, we have

$$\delta \circ g^* = f^* \circ \delta.$$

The proof of (5.6) is essentially the same as (II, 3.10) and hence is omitted.

Finally, let (X, A) denote an arbitrary topological pair and G any given Abelian group.

Consider the inclusion maps

$$i: A \rightarrow X, \qquad j: X \rightarrow (X, A).$$

These inclusion maps induce homomorphisms

$$i^*: H^n(X; G) \rightarrow H^n(A; G),$$

$$j^*: H^n(X, A; G) \rightarrow H^n(X; G)$$

for every integer n. On the other hand, we also have the coboundary operator

$$\delta: H^n(A; G) \rightarrow H^{n+1}(X, A; G)$$

defined for every integer n.

Thus we obtain an upper sequence

$$\cdots \rightarrow H^n(X, A; G) \xrightarrow{j^*} H^n(X; G) \xrightarrow{i^*} H^n(A; G) \xrightarrow{\delta} H^{n+1}(X, A; G) \rightarrow \cdots$$

which will be called the *Alexander cohomology sequence of* (X, A) *over* G.

Proposition 5.7. *The Alexander cohomology sequence of* (X, A) *over* G *is exact.*

The proof of (5.7) is essentially the same as (II, 3.11) and hence is omitted.

EXERCISES

5A. Prove Propositions (5.6) and (5.7).

5B. Prove that the coboundary operator

$$\delta: H^0(A; G) \rightarrow H^1(X, A; G)$$

is the trivial homomorphism if A is connected.

6. Verification of Axioms

Consider the admissible category $\mathscr{C}_T$ of all topological pairs (X, A) and all maps of such pairs. Let G denote an arbitrary Abelian group. Define a collection of three functions

$$\mathscr{H} = \{H, *, \delta\}$$

as follows. For the first function H, we assign to each topological pair (X, A) and each integer q the *q-dimensional Alexander cohomology group*

$$H^q(X, A; G)$$

of the topological pair (X, A) over G. For the second function $*$, we assign to each map $f: (X, A) \to (Y, B)$ in $\mathscr{C}_T$ and each integer q the *induced homomorphism*

$$f^*: H^q(Y, B; G) \to H^q(X, A; G).$$

For the third function δ, we assign to each topological pair (X, A) and each integer q the *coboundary operator*

$$\delta: H^{q-1}(A; G) \to H^q(X, A; G).$$

To establish that this collection $\mathscr{H}$ is a cohomology theory on the category $\mathscr{C}_T$, we have to verify the seven Eilenberg-Steenrod axioms.

By (4.5) and (4.6), $\mathscr{H}$ satisfies the identity axiom (I) and the composition axiom (II). Because of (5.6), $\mathscr{H}$ satisfies the commutativity axiom (III). In view of (5.7), $\mathscr{H}$ satisfies the exactness axiom (IV). Furthermore, $\mathscr{H}$ satisfies the dimension axiom (VII) in accordance with Exercise 2A. It remains to verify the homotopy axiom (V) and the excision axiom (VI).

To verify the excision axiom (VI), let us consider the inclusion map

$$e: (X \backslash U, A \backslash U) \to (X, A),$$

where (X, A) is an arbitrary topological pair and U is any open subset of X satisfying

$$\text{Cl}(U) \subset \text{Int}(A).$$

Lemma 6.1. *The induced homomorphism*

$$C^q(e; G): C^q(X, A; G) \to C^q(X \backslash U, A \backslash U; G)$$

is an isomorphism for every integer q.

   Proof. To prove that $C^q(e; G)$ is an epimorphism, let c denote an arbitrary element of $C^q(X \backslash U, A \backslash U; G)$. Then, by definition, c is an element of $C^q(X \backslash U; G)$ satisfying

$$[C^q(j; G)](c) = 0,$$

where $j: A \setminus U \to X \setminus U$ denotes the inclusion map. Since the natural projection

$$\pi: F^q(X \setminus U; G) \to C^q(X \setminus U; G)$$

is an epimorphism, there is an element $\phi \in F^q(X \setminus U; G)$ with $\pi(\phi) = c$. By definition, ϕ is a function

$$\phi: (X \setminus U)^{q+1} \to G.$$

Extend ϕ to a function $\psi: X^{q+1} \to G$ by taking

$$\psi(x_0, \ldots, x_q) = \begin{cases} \phi(x_0, \ldots, x_q) & \text{(if } x_i \in X \setminus U \text{ for each } i), \\ 0 & \text{(if } x_i \in U \text{ for some } i). \end{cases}$$

By definition, ψ is an element of $F^q(X; G)$. Using the natural projection

$$\rho: F^q(X; G) \to C^q(X; G),$$

we obtain an element

$$d = \rho(\psi) \in C^q(X; G).$$

Since $[C^q(j; G)](c) = 0$, it follows that ϕ is locally zero in $A \setminus U$. By the definition of ψ, this implies that ψ is locally zero in A. Hence we obtain

$$d \in C^q(X, A; G).$$

Since ψ is an extension of ϕ, we obtain

$$[C^q(e; G)](d) = c.$$

This proves that $C^q(e; G)$ is an epimorphism.

To prove that $C^q(e; G)$ is a monomorphism, let c denote an arbitrary element in the kernel of $C^q(e; G) = 0$. As an element of $C^q(X, A; G)$, c is an element of $C^q(X; G)$ saisfying

$$[C^q(i; G)](c) = 0,$$

where $i: A \to X$ denotes the inclusion map. Since ρ is an epimorphism, there is an element $\phi \in F^q(X; G)$ with $\rho(\phi) = c$. By definition, ϕ is a function

$$\phi: X^{q+1} \to G.$$

To prove that ϕ is locally zero in X, let x denote an arbitrary point of X. Since $\text{Cl}(U) \subset \text{Int}(A)$, we have

$$X = [X \setminus \text{Cl}(U)] \cup \text{Int}(A).$$

Hence we have either $x \in X \setminus \text{Cl}(U)$ or $x \in \text{Int}(A)$.

First let us assume $x \in X \backslash \mathrm{Cl}(U)$. Since $[C^q(e; G)](c) = 0$, it follows that the restriction

$$\phi | (X \backslash U)^{q+1}$$

is locally zero. Since $x \in X \backslash U$, there exists an open neighborhood M of x in $X \backslash U$ such that

$$\phi(x_0, x_1, \ldots, x_q) = 0$$

whenever $x_i \in M$ holds for every integer $i = 0, 1, \ldots, q$. Then

$$V = M \cap [X \backslash \mathrm{Cl}(U)]$$

is an open neighborhood of x in X and is contained in M. This proves that ϕ is locally zero at the point x.

Next let us assume $x \in \mathrm{Int}(A)$. Since $[C^q(i; G)](c) = 0$, it follows that the restriction

$$\phi | A^{q+1}$$

is locally zero. Since $x \in \mathrm{Int}(A) \subset A$, there exists an open neighborhood M of X in A such that

$$\phi(x_0, x_1, \ldots, x_q) = 0$$

whenever $x_i \in M$ holds for every $i = 0, 1, \ldots, q$. Then

$$V = M \cap \mathrm{Int}(A)$$

is an open neighborhood of x in X and is contained in M. This proves that ϕ is locally zero at the point x.

Thus we have proved that ϕ is locally zero in X. This implies that

$$c = \rho(\phi) = 0,$$

and hence $C^q(e; G)$ is a monomorphism. $\parallel$

Because of (4.4) and (6.1), $C^q(e; G)$ sends $Z^q(X, A; G)$ isomorphically onto $Z^q(X \backslash U, A \backslash U; G)$ and sends $B^q(X, A; G)$ isomorphically onto $B^q(X \backslash U, A \backslash U; G)$. Consequently, the induced homomorphism

$$e^*: H^q(X, A; G) \to H^q(X \backslash U, A \backslash U; G)$$

is an isomorphism for every integer q. This completes the verification of the excision axiom (VI).

To verify the *homotopy axiom* (V), it suffices to prove that, for any topological pair (X, A), the two canonical imbeddings

$$\kappa_0, \kappa_1: (X, A) \to (X, A) \times I,$$

defined by $\kappa_0(x) = (x, 0)$ and $\kappa_1(x) = (x, 1)$ for every $x \in X$, induce the same homomorphism

$$\kappa_0^* = \kappa_1^*: H^q(X \times I, A \times I; G) \to H^q(X, A; G)$$

for every integer q in accordance with Exercise 1A, Chap. 1.

For this purpose, Spanier gave a very elegant proof based on the description of the Alexander cochain complex as the direct limit of cochain complexes of abstract simplicial complexes. His proof can be found in his book [Sp, pp. 311–314].

Instead of reproducing Spanier's proof for the general case, we shall give an elementary proof for the special case where (X, A) is a *compact pair*; that is, X is a compact space and A is a closed subspace of X.

For this purpose, let ξ denote an arbitrary element of $H^q(X \times I, A \times I; G)$. We have to prove

$$\kappa_0^*(\xi) = \kappa_1^*(\xi).$$

Let $c \in Z^q(X \times I, A \times I; G)$ denote a cocycle which represents the element ξ. Then, by definition, c is an element of the group $C^q(X \times I; G)$ satisfying

$$[C^q(h; G)](c) = 0 \qquad \text{and} \qquad \delta(c) = 0,$$

where $h: A \times I \to X \times I$ denotes the inclusion map. Since the natural projection

$$\pi: F^q(X \times I; G) \to C^q(X \times I; G)$$

is an epimorphism, there exists a function

$$\phi: (X \times I)^{q+1} \to G$$

in $F^q(X \times I; G)$ with $\pi(\phi) = c$.

Since $[C^q(h; G)](c) = 0$ and $\delta(c) = 0$, there exists an open cover α of the space $X \times I$ such that

$$\phi(u_0, u_1, \ldots, u_q) = 0$$

whenever $u_0, u_1, \ldots, u_q$ are contained in $U \cap (A \times I)$ for some $U \in \alpha$ and that

$$[\delta(\phi)](v_0, v_1, \ldots, v_{q+1}) = 0$$

whenever $v_0, v_1, \ldots, v_{q+1}$ are contained in some member U of α.

From the compactness of the spaces X and I, it follows that the existence of an open cover β of X and a finite partition

$$0 = t_0 < t_1 < \cdots < t_{j-1} < t_j < \cdots < t_n = 1$$

of the interval I such that, for every $V \in \beta$ and every $j = 1, 2, \ldots, n$, there is a member $U \in \alpha$ satisfying

$$V \times [t_{j-1}, t_j] \subset U,$$

where $[t_{j-1}, t_j]$ denotes the subinterval of I with t_{j-1} and t_j as end points.
Define a function $\psi: X^q \to G$ by taking

$$\psi(x_0, \ldots, x_{q-1}) = \sum_{j=1}^{n} \sum_{i=0}^{q-1} (-1)^i \, \phi \, [(x_0, t_{j-1}), \ldots, (x_i, t_{j-1}), (x_i, t_j), \ldots, (x_{q-1}, t_j)].$$

Then $\psi | A^q$ is locally zero on A, and $\delta(\psi)$ is locally zero on X. By a direct computation, one can easily verify that the function

$$[F^q(\kappa_0; G)](\phi) - [F^q(\kappa_1; G)](\phi) - \delta(\psi)$$

is locally zero on X. Consequently, we obtain

$$[C^q(\kappa_0; G)](c) - [C^q(\kappa_1; G)](c) = \delta(d),$$

where $d \in C^{q-1}(X, A; G)$ denotes the image $d = \rho(\psi)$ under the natural projection

$$\rho: F^{q-1}(X; G) \to C^{q-1}(X; G).$$

This implies that $\kappa_0^*(\xi) = \kappa_1^*(\xi)$.

Thus we have verified the homotopy axiom (V) for compact pairs (X, A). By Spanier's proof, referred to above, this axiom is also satisfied for every topological pair (X, A). This completes the verification of the Eilenberg-Steenrod axioms for $\mathscr{H}$, and hence $\mathscr{H}$ is a cohomology theory on the category $\mathscr{C}_T$ which is called the *Alexander cohomology theory over G*.

By Exercise 3A, the coefficient group of $\mathscr{H}$ is isomorphic to the given Abelian group G. This proves the existence theorem (Chap. 2, 4.4) once more.

A few special properties of the Alexander cohomology theory are listed as Exercises, although these are by no means easy to prove.

EXERCISES

6A. Consider *fully normal spaces* X, Y and closed subspaces $A \subset X$, $B \subset Y$ [H1, p. 70]. Prove the following *map excision theorem*: If a closed map

$$f: (X, A) \to (Y, B)$$

takes $X \setminus A$ homeomorphically onto $Y \setminus B$, then the induced homomorphism

$$f^*: H^n(Y, B; G) \to H^n(X, A; G)$$

is an isomorphism for every Abelian group G and every integer n.

6B. Establish the following *strong excision theorem*: If A and B are closed subspaces of a fully normal space X, then the induced homomorphism

$$e^*\colon H^n(X, B; G) \to H^n(A, A \cap B; G)$$

of the inclusion map $e\colon (A, A \cap B) \to (X, B)$ is an isomorphism for every Abelian group G and every integer n.

6C. Establish the following *continuity property* of the Alexander cohomology theory: If (X, A) is the limit of an inverse system

$$\mathcal{S} = \{(X_\mu, A_\mu) \mid \mu \in M\}$$

of compact Hausdorff pairs (X_μ, A_μ), then $H^n(X, A; G)$ is isomorphic to the direct limit of the system

$$\{H^n(X_\mu, A_\mu; G) \mid \mu \in M\}.$$

Chapter 4

PRODUCTS

COHOMOLOGY IS RICHER than homology because it has the cup product, of which there is no dual structure in homology. Our objective in the present chapter is a leisurely detailed exposition of the cross product and the cap product, as well as of the important cup product. The cross product can be defined both in homology and in cohomology; the cap product is an operation which connects homology with cohomology. These products will be given in terms of the singular theory and will be based on the Eilenberg-Zilber theorem.

1. Eilenberg-Zilber Theorem

Consider arbitrarily given topological spaces X and Y together with their topological product $X \times Y$. The present section is devoted to an important relation between the singular chain complexes

$$C(X), \qquad C(Y), \qquad C(X \times Y)$$

defined in Sec. 1 of Chap. 2 and in [H5, pp. 210–212].

For every integer n, define an Abelian group $T_n(X, Y)$ as follows: If $n < 0$, we set $T_n(X, Y) = 0$. Otherwise, we define $T_n(X, Y)$ as the direct sum

$$T_n(X, Y) = \sum_{i=1}^{n} C_i(X) \otimes C_{n-1}(Y)$$

of the tensor products $C_i(X) \otimes C_{n-i}(Y)$ defined in [H2, pp. 99–103].

Next, for every integer n, define a homomorphism

$$\partial: T_n(X, Y) \to T_{n-1}(X, Y)$$

as follows: If $n \leq 0$, then $T_{n-1}(X, Y) = 0$, and hence we must have $\partial = 0$.

If $n > 0$, then ∂ is determined by taking

$$\partial(\xi \otimes \eta) = (\partial\xi) \otimes \eta + (-1)^i \xi \otimes (\partial\eta)$$

for every $\xi \in C_i(X)$, every $\eta \in C_{n-i}(Y)$, and every integer $i = 0, 1, \ldots, n$.
The following lemma is obvious.

Lemma 1.1. *For every integer n, the composed homomorphism*

$$\partial^2 = \partial \circ \partial: T_{n+1}(X, Y) \to T_{n-1}(X, Y)$$

of the homomorphisms

$$T_{n+1}(X, Y) \xrightarrow{\partial} T_n(X, Y) \xrightarrow{\partial} T_{n-1}(X, Y)$$

is a trivial homomorphism; that is, $\partial^2 = 0$.

Thus we obtain a chain complex

$$\cdots \to T_{n+1}(X, Y) \xrightarrow{\partial} T_n(X, Y) \xrightarrow{\partial} T_{n-1}(X, Y) \to \cdots$$

which will be referred to as the *tensor product* of the singular chain complexes $C(X)$ and $C(Y)$ and which will be denoted

$$T(X, Y) = C(X) \otimes C(Y).$$

Our objective in the present section is to establish that this chain complex $C(X) \otimes C(Y)$ is *chain equivalent* to the singular chain complex $C(X \times Y)$ of the topological product $X \times Y$.

For this purpose, let us first construct a homomorphism

$$h_n: C_n(X \times Y) \to T_n(X, Y)$$

for every pair (X, Y) of topological spaces and for every integer n such that the following two conditions are satisfied:

(a) For every integer n, the following rectangle is commutative:

$$
\begin{array}{ccc}
C_n(X \times Y) & \xrightarrow{\partial} & C_{n-1}(X \times Y) \\
\downarrow{\scriptstyle h_n} & & \downarrow{\scriptstyle h_{n-1}} \\
T_n(X, Y) & \xrightarrow{\partial} & T_{n-1}(X, Y)
\end{array}
$$

(b) For every integer n and arbitrary maps $f: X \to X'$ and $g: Y \to Y'$, the following rectangle is commutative:

$$
\begin{array}{ccc}
C_n(X \times Y) & \xrightarrow{C_n(f \times g)} & C_n(X' \times Y') \\
\downarrow{\scriptstyle h_n} & & \downarrow{\scriptstyle h_n} \\
T_n(X, Y) & \xrightarrow{T_n(f, g)} & T_n(X', Y')
\end{array}
$$

Here, in condition (b), $C_n(f \times g)$ denotes the induced homomorphism of the topological product

$$f \times g: X \times Y \to X' \times Y'$$

of the maps f and g defined by

$$(f \times g)(x, y) = [f(x), g(y)]$$

for every $x \in X$ and every $y \in Y$. On the other hand, $T_n(f, g)$ stands for the homomorphism defined by the induced homomorphisms

$$C_i(f), \quad C_{n-i}(g) \qquad (i = 0, 1, \dots, n)$$

in the obvious way.

First consider all $n < 0$. Since $T_n(X, Y) = 0$ for every pair (X, Y) of topological spaces, we must have

$$h_n = 0.$$

Conditions (a) and (b) are obviously satisfied for every $n < 0$.

Next assume $n = 0$. Consider the natural projections

$$p: X \times Y \to X, \qquad q: X \times Y \to Y.$$

For every zero-dimensional singular simplex $\sigma: \Delta_0 \to X \times Y$, the composed maps

$$p \circ \sigma: \Delta_0 \to X, \qquad q \circ \sigma: \Delta_0 \to Y$$

are zero-dimensional singular simplexes in X and Y, respectively, and hence we have

$$p \circ \sigma \in C_0(X), \qquad q \circ \sigma \in C_0(Y).$$

Since $C_0(X \times Y)$ is the free Abelian group generated by zero-dimensional singular simplexes in $X \times Y$, the assignment $\sigma \to (p \circ \sigma) \otimes (q \circ \sigma)$ defines a homomorphism

$$h_0: C_0(X \times Y) \to C_0(X) \otimes C_0(Y) = T_0(X, Y).$$

Conditions (a) and (b) are obviously satisfied for every $n \leq 0$.

Finally, let us complete the construction of h_n by induction. For this purpose, let $m > 0$ be any positive integer such that, for every integer $n < m$, h_n has been constructed for all pairs (X, Y) of topological spaces in such a way that conditions (a) and (b) are satisfied.

Consider the diagonal imbedding

$$d_m: \Delta_m \to \Delta_m \times \Delta_m$$

defined by $d_m(t) = (t, t)$ for every point t of Δ_m. Then d_m is an m-dimensional singular simplex in the space $\Delta_m \times \Delta_m$ and hence is an element of the group $C_m(\Delta_m \times \Delta_m)$. Since

$$\partial(d_m) \in C_{m-1}(\Delta_m \times \Delta_m),$$

it follows from our inductive assumption that the element

$$h_{m-1}[\partial(d_m)] \in T_{m-1}(\Delta_m, \Delta_m)$$

has been constructed. By condition (a), we have

$$\partial\{h_{m-1}[\partial(d_m)]\} = h_{m-2}[(\partial \circ \partial)(d_m)] = 0.$$

By means of the Künneth formula in homological algebra [H6, Chap. III, (6.7)], this implies the existence of an element

$$e_m \in T_m(\Delta_m, \Delta_m)$$

satisfying

$$\partial(e_m) = h_{m-1}[\partial(d_m)].$$

Having selected $e_m \in T_m(\Delta_m, \Delta_m)$, we define for any pair (X, Y) of topological spaces a function

$$f_m: S_m(X \times Y) \to T_m(X, Y)$$

as follows. Let $\sigma \in S_m(X \times Y)$ be arbitrarily given. Then σ is a map

$$\sigma: \Delta_m \to X \times Y.$$

The composed maps

$$\xi = p \circ \sigma: \Delta_m \to X, \qquad \eta = q \circ \sigma: \Delta_m \to Y$$

of σ and the natural projections $p: X \times Y \to X$, $q: X \times Y \to Y$ induce a homomorphism

$$T_m(\xi, \eta): T_m(\Delta_m, \Delta_m) \to T_m(X, Y)$$

in the obvious way. Then we define

$$f_m(\sigma) = [T_m(\xi, \eta)](e_m).$$

Since $C_m(X \times Y)$ is the free Abelian group generated by $S_m(X \times Y)$, this function f_m extends to a unique homomorphism

$$h_m: C_m(X \times Y) \to T_m(X, Y).$$

The verification of conditions (a) and (b) is straightforward and hence is omitted. This completes the inductive construction of h_n.

Because of condition (a), the sequence

$$h = \{ h_n \mid n \in Z \}$$

of homomorphisms is a *chain homomorphism* from the chain complex $C(X \times Y)$ into the chain complex $T(X, Y)$ and will be denoted by

$$h: C(X \times Y) \rightarrow C(X) \otimes C(Y).$$

Because of condition (b), this chain homomorphism h is said to be *natural* or *functional*. Thus we have proved the following lemma.

Lemma 1.2. *There exists a functional chain homomorphism*

$$h: C(X \times Y) \rightarrow C(X) \otimes C(Y)$$

defined for every pair (X, Y) of topological spaces and satisfying

$$h_0(\sigma) = (p \circ \sigma) \otimes (q \circ \sigma)$$

for every zero-dimensional singular simplex σ in $X \times Y$, where

$$p: X \times Y \rightarrow X, \qquad q: X \times Y \rightarrow Y$$

denote the natural projections.

Similarly, one can establish the following lemma by means of the fact that $C(\Delta_n \times \Delta_n)$ is acyclic and that $T_n(X, Y)$ is the free Abelian group generated by the set

$$S_n(X, Y) = \{ \xi \otimes \eta \mid \xi \in S_i(X), \eta \in S_{n-i}(Y), i = 0, 1, \ldots, n \}.$$

Lemma 1.3. *There exists a functorial chain homomorphism*

$$k: C(X) \otimes C(Y) \rightarrow C(X \times Y)$$

defined for every pair (X, Y) of topological spaces and satisfying

$$k_0(\xi \otimes \eta) = \xi \times \eta$$

for arbitrary zero-dimensional singular simplexes $\xi: \Delta_0 \rightarrow X$ and $\eta: \Delta_0 \rightarrow Y$, where

$$\xi \times \eta: \Delta_0 \rightarrow X \times Y$$

denotes the (restricted) topological product of ξ and η defined by

$$(\xi \times \eta)(t) = [\xi(t), \eta(t)] \qquad (t \in \Delta_0).$$

Next let us establish the following lemma.

Lemma 1.4. *For any functorial chain homomorphism*

$$h: C(X \times Y) \to C(X) \otimes C(Y)$$

in (1.2) *and any functorial chain homomorphism*

$$k: C(X) \otimes C(Y) \to C(X \times Y)$$

in (1.3), *the composed chain homomorphisms $k \circ h$ and $h \circ k$ are chain homotopic to the identity chain homomorphisms on the chain complexes $C(X \times Y)$ and $C(X) \otimes C(Y)$, respectively.*

Proof. To prove that $k \circ h$ is chain homotopic to the identity on $C(X \times Y)$, we shall construct a homomorphism

$$D_n: C_n(X \times Y) \to C_{n+1}(X \times Y)$$

for every pair (X, Y) of topological spaces and every integer n satisfying the following two conditions:

(a)   For every integer n and every element of c of $C_n(X \times Y)$, we have

$$\partial[D_n(c)] + D_{n-1}[\partial(c)] = k \circ h.$$

(b)   For arbitrary maps $f: X \to X'$, $g: Y \to Y'$ and every integer n, the following rectangle is commutative:

$$
\begin{array}{ccc}
C_n(X \times Y) & \xrightarrow{\;D_n\;} & C_{n+1}(X \times Y) \\
\Big\downarrow{\scriptstyle C_n(f \times g)} & & \Big\downarrow{\scriptstyle C_{n+1}(f \times g)} \\
C_n(X' \times Y') & \xrightarrow{\;D_n\;} & C_{n+1}(X' \times Y')
\end{array}
$$

where $f \times g: X \times Y \to X' \times Y'$ denotes the topological product of f and g.

First let us consider all $n \leq 0$. In this case, since $k_n \circ h_n$ is the identity homomorphism, we may take $D_n = 0$. Conditions (a) and (b) are obviously satisfied for every $n \leq 0$.

To complete the construction of D_n by induction, let m denote any positive integer such that, for every $n < m$, D_n has been constructed for every pair (X, Y) of topological spaces in such a way that conditions (a) and (b) are satisfied.

Consider the diagonal imbedding

$$d_m: \Delta_m \to \Delta_m \times \Delta_m$$

as a singular m-simplex in the space $\Delta_m \times \Delta_m$ and hence as an element of the group $C_m(\Delta_m \times \Delta_m)$. Since

$$\partial(d_m) \in C_{m-1}(\Delta_m \times \Delta_m),$$

it follows from our inductive assumption that we have

$$(k_{m-1} \circ h_{m-1})[\partial(d_m)] - \partial(d_m) = \partial[D_{m-1}(\partial d_m)]$$

because of $\partial[\partial(d_m)] = 0$. Hence we obtain

$$\partial\{(k_m \circ h_m)(d_m) - d_m - D_{m-1}[\partial(d_m)]\}$$
$$= (k_{m-1} \circ h_{m-1})[\partial(d_m)] - \partial(d_m) - \partial[D_{m-1}(\partial d_m)] = 0.$$

It follows that the element

$$(k_m \circ h_n)(d_m) - d_m - D_{m-1}[\partial(d_m)]$$

of $C_m(\Delta_m \times \Delta_m)$ is a cycle. Since $\Delta_m \times \Delta_m$ is homeomorphic to a starlike subspace of a Euclidean space, the sequence

$$C_{m+1}(\Delta_m \times \Delta_m) \xrightarrow{\partial} C_m(\Delta_m \times \Delta_m) \xrightarrow{\partial} C_{m-1}(\Delta_m \times \Delta_m)$$

is exact according to Exercise 3A, Chap. 2. Hence there exists an element e_m of $C_{m+1}(\Delta_m \times \Delta_m)$ satisfying

$$\partial(e_m) = (k_m \circ h_m)(d_m) - d_m - D_{m-1}[\partial(d_m)].$$

Having selected $e_m \in C_{m+1}(\Delta_m \times \Delta_m)$, we define a function

$$F_m: S_m(X \times Y) \to C_{m+1}(X \times Y)$$

as follows. Let $\sigma \in S_m(X \times Y)$ be arbitrarily given. Then σ is a map

$$\sigma: \Delta_m \to X \times Y.$$

The topological product

$$\xi \times \eta : \Delta_m \times \Delta_m \longrightarrow X \times Y$$

of the composed maps

$$\xi = p \circ \sigma : \Delta_m \to X, \qquad \eta = q \circ \sigma : \Delta_m \to Y$$

induces a homomorphism

$$C_{m+1}(\xi \times \eta) : C_{m+1}(\Delta_m \times \Delta_m) \to C_{m+1}(X \times Y).$$

Then we define

$$D_m(\sigma) = [C_{m+1}(\xi \times \eta)](e_m).$$

Since $C_m(X \times Y)$ is the free Abelian group generated by $S_m(X \times Y)$, this function F_m extends to a unique homomorphism

$$D_m: C_m(X \times Y) \to C_{m+1}(X \times Y).$$

The verification of conditions (a) and (b) is straightforward and hence is omitted. This completes the inductive construction of D_n.

Because of condition (a), the sequence

$$D = \{D_n \mid n \in Z\}$$

is a chain homotopy between $k \circ h$ and the identity chain homomorphism on $C(X \times Y)$.

Similarly, one can prove that $h \circ k$ is chain homotopic to the identity chain homomorphism on $C(X) \otimes C(Y)$. ‖

The following corollary is a direct consequence of the lemmas (1.1) through (1.3).

Corollary 1.5 (*Eilenberg-Zilber Theorem*). *The chain complexes* $C(X \times Y)$ *and* $C(X) \otimes C(Y)$ *are chain equivalent.*

EXERCISES
1A. Prove that every chain homomorphism

$$h: C(X \times Y) \to C(X) \otimes C(Y)$$

in (1.1) induces isomorphisms

$$h_*: H_n(X \times Y; G) \approx H_n[C(X) \otimes C(Y); G],$$

$$h^*: H^n[C(X) \otimes C(Y); G] \approx H^n(X \times Y; G)$$

for every integer n and every Abelian group G.

1B. Prove that the isomorphisms h_* and h^* in Exercise 1A are independent of the particular choice of the chain homomorphism h in (1.1).

2. Künneth Formula

Throughout the present section, let X and Y denote arbitrarily given topological spaces. By the Eilenberg-Zilber theorem (1.5), we have

$$H_n(X \times Y) \approx H_n[C(X) \otimes C(Y)]$$

for every integer n. On the other hand, we have

$$H_n[C(X) \otimes C(Y)] \approx \{H(X) \otimes H(Y)\}_n \oplus \{\mathrm{Tor}[H(X), H(Y)]\}_{n-1}$$

according to the Künneth formula in homological algebra [H6, Chap. III, (6.7)]. Here, $\oplus$ is the symbol for direct sum, while $\{H(X) \otimes H(Y)\}_n$ and $\{\mathrm{Tor}[H(X), H(Y)]\}_{n-1}$ denote the following direct sums:

$$\{H(X) \otimes H(Y)\}_n = \sum_{i=0}^{n} H_i(X) \otimes H_{n-i}(Y),$$

$$\{\mathrm{Tor}[H(X), H(Y)]\}_{n-1} = \sum_{i=0}^{n-1} \mathrm{Tor}[H_i(X), H_{n-1-i}(Y)].$$

Thus we obtain the following theorem, known as the *Künneth formula for integral singular homology groups*.

Theorem 2.1. *For every integer* $n \geqslant 0$, *we have*

$$H_n(X \times Y) \approx \{H(X) \otimes H(Y)\}_n \oplus \{\text{Tor}[H(X), H(Y)]\}_{n-1}.$$

In view of the *universal coefficient theorems* in homological algebra, (2.1) solves the problem of finding the singular homology and cohomology groups of the topological product $X \times Y$. In fact, the following theorem is a direct consequence of [H6, Chap. III, (5.1) and (5.6)] and is known as the *universal coefficient theorem* for singular homology and cohomology groups.

Theorem 2.2. *For every topological space* W, *every Abelian group* G, *and every integer* $n \geqslant 0$, *we have*

$$H_n(W; G) \approx \{H_n(W) \otimes G\} \oplus \{\text{Tor}[H_{n-1}(W), G]\},$$

$$H^n(W; G) \approx \text{Hom}[H_n(W), G] \oplus \text{Ext}[H_{n-1}(W), G].$$

However, there are generalizations of (2.1) for the singular homology and cohomology groups with arbitrarily given coefficient groups. These are direct consequences of theorems in homological algebra and will be stated as follows.

The following theorem is a direct consequence of [H6, Chap. III, (7.1)] and is known as the *Künneth formula for singular homology groups*.

Theorem 2.3. *For any two Abelian groups* F, G *satisfying* $\text{Tor}(F, G) = 0$ *and every integer* $n \geqslant 0$, *we have*

$$H_n(X \times Y; F \otimes G) \approx \{H(X; F) \otimes H(Y; G)\}_n \otimes \{\text{Tor}[H(X; F), H(Y; G)]\}_{n-1}.$$

If Y is a singleton space and F is the additive group Z of all integers, (2.3) reduces to the following corollary, which is the homology part of the *universal coefficient theorem* (2.2).

Corollary 2.4. *For every Abelian group* G *and every integer* n, *we have*

$$H_n(X; G) \approx \{H_n(X) \otimes G\} \oplus \{\text{Tor}[H_{n-1}(X), G]\}.$$

A topological space W is said to be of *finite homology type* iff $H_n(W)$ is finitely generated for every integer n. Hence every finite cellular polytope is of finite homology type.

The following theorem is a direct consequence of [H6, Chap. III, (7.2)] and is known as the *Künneth formula for singular cohomology groups*.

Theorem 2.5. *For any two Abelian groups F, G satisfying* $\text{Tor}(F, G) = 0$ *and every integer $n \geq 0$, we have*

$$H^n(X \times Y; F \otimes G) \approx \{H^*(X; F) \otimes H^*(Y; G)\}^n \oplus \{\text{Tor}[H^*(X; F), H^*(Y; G)]\}^{n+1}$$

provided that at least one of the following two conditions is satisfied:

(a) *Both X and Y are of finite homology type.*

(b) *Y is of finite homology type and G is finitely generated.*

Here, $\oplus$ is the symbol for direct sum and

$$\{H^*(X; F) \otimes H^*(Y; G)\}^n = \sum_{i=0}^{n} H^i(X; F) \otimes H^{n-i}(Y; G),$$

$$\{\text{Tor}[H^*(X; F), H^*(Y; G)]\}^{n+1} = \sum_{i=0}^{n+1} \text{Tor}[H^i(X; F), H^{n+1-i}(Y; G)].$$

If Y is a singleton space and F is the additive group Z of all integers, then (2.5) reduces to the following corollary.

Corollary 2.6. *For every integer $n \geq 0$, we have*

$$H^n(X; G) \approx [H^n(X) \otimes G] \oplus \text{Tor}[H^{n+1}(X), G],$$

provided that at least one of the following two conditions is satisfied:

(a) *The topological space X is of finite homology type.*

(b) *The Abelian group G is finitely generated.*

EXERCISES

2A. Let (X, A) and (Y, B) denote any two topological pairs such that

$$(X \times Y; A \times Y, X \times B)$$

is a *proper triad* in the sense of [H5, p. 88]. Prove that every functorial chain homomorphism h in (1.2) induces a chain equivalence of

$$C(X \times Y)/C[(A \times Y) \cup (X \times B)]$$

with the tensor product

$$[C(X)/C(A)] \otimes [C(Y)/C(B)].$$

Then establish the *Künneth formula for relative integral singular homology groups*, which states that the group

$$H_n[X \times Y, (A \times Y) \cup (X \times B)]$$

is isomorphic to the direct sum

$$\{H(X, A) \otimes H(Y, B)\}_n \oplus \{\mathrm{Tor}[H(X, A), H(Y, B)]\}_{n-1}.$$

2B. Extend (2.3) and (2.5) to topological pairs (X, A) and (Y, B) such that $(X \times Y, A \times Y, X \times B)$ is a proper triad.

2C. Extend (2.4) and (2.6) to an arbitrary topological pair (X, A).

3. Cross Products

Throughout the present section, let X, Y denote arbitrarily given topological spaces and F, G any additive Abelian groups. Our objective is the construction of a functorial homomorphism.

$$\pi^*\colon H^p(X; F) \otimes H^q(Y; G) \to H^{p+q}(X \times Y; F \otimes G)$$

for every $p \geqslant 0$ and every $q \geqslant 0$.

For this purpose, let us consider the singular cochain complexes

$$C^*(X; F), \qquad C^*(Y; G), \qquad C^*(X \times Y; F \otimes G)$$

as defined in Sec. 2, Chap. 2.

For every integer n, define an Abelian group $T^n(X, Y; F, G)$ as follows: If $n < 0$, we set

$$T^n(X, Y; F, G) = 0.$$

Otherwise, we define $T^n(X, Y; F, G)$ as the direct sum

$$T^n(X, Y; F, G) = \sum_{i=0}^{n} C^i(X; F) \otimes C^{n-i}(Y; G)$$

of the tensor products $C^i(X; F) \otimes C^{n-i}(Y; G)$ defined in [H2, pp. 99–103].

Next, for every integer n, define a homomorphism

$$\delta\colon T^n(X, Y; F, G) \to T^{n+1}(X, Y; F, G)$$

as follows: If $n < 0$, then $T^n(X, Y; F, G) = 0$, and hence we must have $\delta > 0$. If $n \geqslant 0$, then δ is determined by taking

$$\delta(\xi \otimes \eta) = (\delta\xi) \otimes \eta + (-1)^i \xi \otimes (\delta\eta)$$

for every $\xi \in C^i(X; F)$, every $\eta \in C^{n-i}(Y; G)$, and every integer $i = 1, \ldots, n$.

The following lemma is obvious.

Lemma 3.1. *For every integer n, the composed homomorphism*

$$\delta^2 = \delta \circ \delta: T^{n-1}(X, Y; F, G) \to T^{n+1}(X, Y; F, G)$$

of the homomorphisms

$$T^{n-1}(X, Y; F, G) \xrightarrow{\delta} T^n(X, Y; F, G) \xrightarrow{\delta} T^{n+1}(X, Y; F, G)$$

is a trivial homomorphism; that is, $\delta^2 = 0$.

Thus we obtain a cochain complex

$$\cdots \to T^{n-1}(X, Y; F, G) \xrightarrow{\delta} T^n(X, Y; F, G) \xrightarrow{\delta} T^{n+1}(X, Y; F, G) \to \cdots$$

which will be referred to as the *tensor product* of the singular cochain complexes $C^*(X; F)$ and $C^*(Y; G)$ and which will be denoted by

$$T^*(X, Y; F, G) = C^*(X; F) \otimes C^*(Y; G).$$

For every pair of integers $p \geqslant 0$ and $q \geqslant 0$, let us define a homomorphism

$$\rho^*: H^p(X; F) \otimes H^q(Y; G) \to H^{p+q}[C^*(X; F) \otimes C^*(Y; G)]$$

as follows.

Let $\xi \in H^p(X; F)$ and $\eta \in H^q(Y; G)$ be arbitrarily given elements. These are cosets of $B^p(X; F)$ and $B^q(Y; G)$ in $Z^p(X; F)$ and $Z^q(Y; G)$, respectively. Let

$$x \in \xi \subset Z^p(X; F) \subset C^p(X; F),$$

$$y \in \eta \subset Z^q(Y; G) \subset C^q(Y; G).$$

Then $x \otimes y$ is an element of

$$C^p(X; F) \otimes C^q(Y; G) \subset T^{p+q}(X, Y; F, G).$$

Since $\delta x = 0$ and $\delta y = 0$, we have

$$\delta(x \otimes y) = \delta x \otimes y + (-1)^p x \otimes \delta y = 0.$$

This implies that $x \otimes y$ is in the subgroup $Z^{p+q}[C^*(X; F) \otimes C^*(Y; G)]$ of $T^{p+q}(X, Y; F, G)$ and hence determines an element

$$\zeta \in H^{p+q}[C^*(X; F) \otimes C^*(Y; G)].$$

One can easily verify that this element ζ of $H^{p+q}[C^*(X; F) \otimes C^*(Y; G)]$ does not depend on the choices of the cocycles x and y from the cosets ξ and η, respectively. Consequently, ζ is completely determined by the elements ξ and η. It is straightforward to verify that the assignment $\xi \otimes \eta \to \zeta$ determines a homomorphism

$$\rho^*: H^p(X; F) \otimes H^q(Y; F) \to H^{p+q}[C^*(X; F) \otimes C^*(Y; G)].$$

Next we recall that

$$C^p(X; F) = \text{Hom}[C_p(X), F],$$

$$C^q(Y; G) = \text{Hom}[C^q(Y), G]$$

are Abelian groups of homomorphisms. For any two integers p and q, there is a homomorphism

$$\mu^{pq} \colon C^p(X; F) \otimes C^q(Y; G) \to \text{Hom}[C_p(X) \otimes C_q(Y), F \otimes G]$$

determined by

$$[\mu^{pq}(\phi \otimes \psi)](x \otimes y) = \phi(x) \otimes \psi(y)$$

for every $\phi \in C^p(X; F)$, $\psi \in C^q(Y; G)$, $x \in C_p(X)$, and $y \in C^q(Y)$. One can easily see that these homomorphisms μ^{pq} define a cochain homomorphism

$$\mu \colon C^*(X; F) \otimes C^*(Y; G) \to \text{Hom}[C(X) \otimes C(Y), F \otimes G]$$

from the cochain complex $C^*(X; F) \otimes C^*(Y; G)$ into the cochain complex

$$C^*[C(X) \otimes C(Y); F \otimes G] = \text{Hom}[C(X) \otimes C(Y), F \otimes G].$$

This cochain·homomorphism μ induces a homomorphism

$$\mu^* \colon H^n[C^*(X; F) \otimes C^*(Y; G)] \to H^n[C(X) \otimes C(Y); F \otimes G]$$

for every integer n.

Finally, it follows from the Eilenberg-Zilber theorem that every functorial chain homomorphism

$$h \colon C(X \times Y) \to C(X) \otimes C(Y)$$

in (1.2) induces an isomorphism

$$h^* \colon H^n[C(X) \otimes C(Y); F \otimes G] \to H^n(X \times Y; F \otimes G)$$

for every integer n. According to Exercise 1A, h^* does not depend on the choice of the chain homomorphism h.

Composing ρ^*, μ^*, and h^* with $n = p + q$, we obtain a homomorphism

$$\pi^* = h^* \circ \mu^* \circ \rho^* \colon H^p(X; F) \otimes H^q(Y; G) \to H^{p+q}(X \times Y; F \otimes G)$$

for every $p \geq 0$ and every $q \geq 0$.

For every $\xi \in H^p(X; F)$ and every $\eta \in H^q(Y; G)$, the element $\pi^*(\xi \otimes \eta)$ of $H^{p+q}(X \times Y; F \otimes G)$ will be referred to as the *cross product* of ξ and η and will be denoted by the symbol

$$\xi \times \eta.$$

Since ρ^*, μ, and h are functorial, the following proposition is obvious.

Proposition 3.2. *For arbitrary maps f: $X \to X'$ and g: $Y \to Y'$, the following rectangle is commutative:*

$$H^p(X'; F) \otimes H^q(Y'; G) \xrightarrow{\ \pi^*\ } H^{p+q}(X' \times Y'; F \otimes G)$$

$$\downarrow{\scriptstyle f^* \otimes g^*} \qquad\qquad\qquad \downarrow{\scriptstyle (f \times g)^*}$$

$$H^p(X; F) \otimes H^q(Y; G) \xrightarrow{\ \pi^*\ } H^{p+q}(X \times Y; F \otimes G)$$

Hence, for every $\xi \in H^p(X'; F)$ and every $\eta \in H^q(Y'; G)$, we have

$$(f \times g)^*(\xi \times \eta) = f^*(\xi) \times g^*(\eta).$$

Next let us consider three arbitrary topological spaces X, Y, and Z. There are natural isomorphisms

$$i: C[(X \times Y) \times Z] \approx C[X \times (Y \times Z)],$$

$$j: [C(X) \otimes C(Y) \otimes C(Z)] \approx C(X) \otimes [C(Y) \otimes C(Z)].$$

On the other hand, there are chain equivalences

$$h: C[(X \times Y) \times Z] \to [C(X) \otimes C(Y)] \otimes C(Z),$$

$$k: C[X \times (Y \times Z)] \to C(X) \otimes [C(Y) \otimes C(Z)]$$

because of the Eilenberg-Zilber theorem. Furthermore, one can also show that $k \circ i$ and $j \circ h$ are chain homotopic. As a consequence of this, we have the following proposition.

Proposition 3.3. *The cross product is associative; that is, for arbitrary elements*

$$\xi \in H^p(X; F), \qquad \eta \in H^q(Y; G), \qquad \zeta \in H^r(Z; H),$$

we have

$$(\xi \times \eta) \times \zeta = \xi \times (\eta \times \zeta)$$

in the group $H^{p+q+r}(X \times Y \times Z; F \otimes G \otimes H)$.

Now let us consider the homeomorphism

$$\tau: Y \times X \to X \times Y$$

defined by $\tau(y, x) = (x, y)$ for every $x \in X$ and every $y \in Y$. This homeomorphism τ induces an isomorphism

$$\tau^*: H^n(X \times Y; F \otimes G) \approx H^n(Y \times X; F \otimes G)$$

for every integer n.

On the other hand, consider the isomorphism

$$\theta\colon G \otimes F \approx F \otimes G$$

determined by taking $\theta(g \otimes f) = f \otimes g$ for every $f \in F$ and $g \in G$. This isomorphism induces an isomorphism

$$\theta^{\#}\colon C^n(Y \times X; G \otimes F) \approx C^n(Y \times X; F \otimes G)$$

defined by $\theta^{\#}(\phi) = \theta \circ \phi$ for every cochain

$$\phi\colon C_n(Y \times X) \to G \otimes F$$

in $C^n(Y \times X; G \otimes F)$. Since $\theta^{\#}$ commutes with the coboundary operator δ, it induces an isomorphism

$$\theta^*\colon H^n(Y \times X; G \otimes F) \approx H^n(Y \times X; F \otimes G)$$

for every integer n.

Proposition 3.4. *For every* $\xi \in H^p(X; F)$ *and every* $\eta \in H^q(Y; G)$, *we have*

$$\tau^*(\xi \times \eta) = (-1)^{pq}\theta^*(\eta \times \xi).$$

Proof. The homeomorphism τ induces a chain isomorphism

$$\tau_{\#}\colon C(Y \times X) \approx C(X \times Y).$$

According to the Eilenberg-Zilber theorem, there are functorial chain equivalences

$$h\colon C(X \times Y) \to C(X) \otimes C(Y),$$

$$k\colon C(Y \times X) \to C(Y) \otimes C(X).$$

For every $p \geqslant 0$ and every $q \geqslant 0$, define an isomorphism

$$\sigma_{pq}\colon C_p(X) \otimes C_q(Y) \approx C_q(Y) \otimes C_p(X)$$

by taking

$$\sigma_{pq}(\xi \otimes \eta) = (-1)^{pq}(\eta \otimes \xi)$$

for every $\xi \in C_p(X)$ and every $\eta \in C_q(Y)$. By means of the definitions of the chain complexes $C(X) \otimes C(Y)$ and $C(Y) \otimes C(X)$, one can easily verify that these isomorphisms σ_{pq} define a chain isomorphism

$$\sigma\colon C(X) \otimes C(Y) \approx C(Y) \otimes C(X).$$

As in the proof of (1.4), one can prove that the two composed chain homomorphisms

$$\sigma \circ h, \ k \circ \tau_{\#}^{-1}: \ C(X \times Y) \to C(Y) \otimes C(X)$$

are chain homotopic. Then it is straightforward to verify that

$$\tau^*(\xi \times \eta) = (-1)^{pq}\theta^*(\eta \times \xi)$$

by means of the definition of the cross products. ‖

The property of cross products in (3.4) is referred to in the literature as *anticommutativity*. Perhaps, *signed commutativity* is a more satisfactory term.

EXERCISES

3A. Dualize the construction given in the text to obtain a functorial homomorphism

$$\pi_*: H_p(X; F) \otimes H_q(Y; G) \to H_{p+q}(X \times Y; F \otimes G)$$

for every $p \geqslant 0$ and every $q \geqslant 0$. For every $\xi \in H_p(X; F)$ and every $\eta \in H_q(Y; G)$, the element

$$\xi \times \eta = \pi_*(\xi \otimes \eta)$$

in $H_{p+q}(X \times Y; F \otimes G)$ is called the *cross product* of ξ and η. Establish the duals of propositions (3.2) through (3.4).

3B. Let (X, A) and (Y, B) denote any two topological pairs such that

$$(X \times Y; A \times Y, X \times B)$$

is a *proper triad* in the sense of [H5, p. 88]. Let

$$C = (A \times Y) \cup (X \times B).$$

With the aid of Exercise 2A, generalize the construction given in the text to obtain a functorial homomorphism

$$\pi^*: H^p(X, A; F) \otimes H^q(Y, B; G) \to H^{p+q}(X \times Y, C; F \otimes G)$$

for every $p \geqslant 0$ and every $q \geqslant 0$. For every $\xi \in H^p(X, A; F)$ and every $\eta \in V^q(Y, B; G)$, the element

$$\xi \times \eta = \pi^*(\xi \otimes \eta)$$

in $H^{p+q}(X \times Y, C; F \otimes G)$ is called the *cross product* of ξ and η. Generalize propositions (3.2) through (3.4).

3C. Dualize the construction in Exercise 3B to obtain a functorial homomorphism

$$\pi_*: H_p(X, A; F) \otimes H_q(Y, B; G) \to H_{p+q}(X \times Y, C; F \otimes G)$$

for every $p \geqslant 0$ and every $q \geqslant 0$. For every $\xi \in H_p(X, A; F)$ and every $\eta \in H_q(Y, B; G)$, the element

$$\xi \times \eta = \pi_*(\xi \otimes \eta)$$

in $H_{p+q}(X \times Y, C; F \otimes G)$ is called the *cross product* of ξ and η. Establish properties corresponding to propositions (3.2) through (3.4).

4. Cup Products

By a *pairing* of two Abelian groups F and G to an Abelian group K, we mean a homomorphism

$$\omega: F \otimes G \to K$$

of the tensor product $F \otimes G$ into K.

Examples of pairings:

(a) Let $K = F \otimes G$. The identity homomorphism

$$\iota: F \otimes G \to F \otimes G$$

is a pairing of F and G to $F \otimes G$.

(b) Let $F = Z$ and $K = G$, where Z denotes the additive group of all integers. The homomorphism

$$\omega: Z \otimes G \to G,$$

defined by $\omega(n \otimes g) = ng$ for every $n \in Z$ and every $g \in G$, is a pairing of Z and G to G.

(c) Let $F = \text{Hom}(G, K)$ as defined in [H2, p. 109]. The homomorphism

$$\omega: F \otimes G \to K,$$

defined by $\omega(f \otimes g) = f(g)$ for every $f \in F$ and every $g \in G$, is a pairing of F and G to K.

(d) Let R denote a ring as defined in [H2, p. 114]. The homomorphism

$$\omega: R \otimes R \to R$$

of the tensor product $R \otimes R$ of R and R as Abelian groups to R itself, defined by

$$\omega(x \otimes y) = xy$$

for arbitrary $x \in R$ and $y \in R$, is a pairing of the Abelian groups R and R to R.

Throughout the remainder of the present section, let

$$\omega: F \otimes G \to K$$

denote an arbitrarily given pairing of F and G to K.

For every topological space X, consider the diagonal imbedding

$$d: X \to X \times X$$

defined by $d(x) = (x, x)$ for every $x \in X$. This map d induces a homomorphism

$$d^*: H^n(X \times X; F \otimes G) \to H^n(X; F \otimes G)$$

for every integer n.

On the other hand, the homomorphism $\omega: F \otimes G \to K$ induces a homomorphism

$$\omega^\#: C^n(X; F \otimes G) \to C^n(X; K)$$

for every integer n defined by

$$\omega^\#(\phi) = \omega \circ \phi$$

for every cochain $\phi: C_n(X) \to F \otimes G$ in the group

$$C^n(X; F \otimes G) = \mathrm{Hom}[C_n(X), F \otimes G].$$

Since $\omega^\#$ commutes with the coboundary operator δ, it induces a homomorphism

$$\omega^*: H^n(X; F \otimes G) \to H^n(X; K)$$

for every integer n.

Composing the homomorphism

$$\pi^*: H^p(X; F) \otimes H^q(X; G) \to H^{p+q}(X \times X; F \otimes G)$$

constructed in the preceding section with the homomorphisms

$$d^*: H^{p+q}(X \times X; F \otimes G) \to H^{p+q}(X; F \otimes G),$$

$$\omega^*: H^{p+q}(X; F \otimes G) \to H^{p+q}(X; K),$$

we obtain a homomorphism

$$\smile = \omega^* \circ d^* \circ \pi^*: H^p(X; F) \otimes H^q(X; G) \to H^{p+q}(X; K)$$

for every $p \geqslant 0$ and every $q \geqslant 0$.

For every $\xi \in H(X; F)$ and every $\eta \in H^q(X; G)$, the element

$$\smile (\xi \otimes \eta) = (\omega^* \circ d^*)[\pi^*(\xi \otimes \eta)] = (\omega^* \circ d^*)(\xi \times \eta)$$

of the group $H^{p+q}(X; K)$, where $\xi \times \eta$ denotes the cross product of ξ and η will be simply denoted by the symbol

$$\xi \smile \eta$$

and will be referred to as the *cup product* of ξ and η with respect to the given pairing ω.

Proposition 4.1.   *For every map f: $X \to Y$, every $\xi \in H^p(Y; F)$, and every $\eta \in H^q(Y; G)$, we have*

$$f^*(\xi \smile \eta) = f^*(\xi) \smile f^*(\eta)$$

in the group $H^{p+q}(X; K)$.

Proof.   According to (3.2), we have

$$(f \times f)^*(\xi \times \eta) = f^*(\xi) \times f^*(\eta).$$

Because of the commutativity of the rectangle

$$
\begin{array}{ccc}
X & \xrightarrow{\ \ d\ \ } & X \times X \\
\downarrow{\scriptstyle f} & & \downarrow{\scriptstyle f \times f} \\
Y & \xrightarrow{\ \ d\ \ } & Y \times Y
\end{array}
$$

of maps, we have

$$d^* \circ (f \times f)^* = f^* \circ d^*.$$

Finally, by the definitions of f^* and ω^*, one can easily see that we have

$$\omega^* \circ f^* = f^* \circ \omega^*.$$

Hence we obtain

$$f^*(\xi \smile \eta) = (f^* \circ \omega^* \circ d^*)(\xi \times \eta)$$
$$= (\omega^* \circ f^* \circ d^*)(\xi \times \eta)$$
$$= (\omega^* \circ d^*)[(f \times f)^*(\xi \times \eta)]$$

$$= (\omega^* \circ d^*)[f^*(\xi) \times f^*(\eta)]$$

$$= f^*(\xi) \smile f^*(\eta).$$

This completes the proof of (4.1). ‖

For other properties of the cup products, let us consider the important special case where the coefficient group is a ring R, as defined in [H2, p. 114], which is commutative. We shall be concerned with the cup products with respect to the pairing

$$\omega: R \otimes R \to R$$

given in example (d) above.

The following proposition is an immediate consequence of (3.3) and the associativity of the ring R.

Proposition 4.2. *The cup product is associative; that is, for arbitrary elements*

$$\xi \in H^p(X; R), \qquad \eta \in H^q(X; R), \qquad \zeta \in H^r(X; R),$$

we have

$$(\xi \smile \eta) \smile \zeta = \xi \smile (\eta \smile \zeta)$$

in the group $H^{p+q+r}(X; R)$.

Since $\tau \circ d = d$, the following proposition is an immediate consequence of (3.4) and the commutativity of the ring R.

Proposition 4.3. *For every* $\xi \in H^p(X; R)$ *and every* $\eta \in H^q(X; R)$, *we have*

$$\xi \smile \eta = (-1)^{pq}(\eta \smile \xi)$$

in the group $H^{p+q}(X; R)$.

Next let us consider the direct sum

$$H^*(X; R) = \sum_{n=0}^{\infty} H^n(X; R)$$

as defined in [H2, p. 77]. Then, for every $n \geq 0$, $H^n(X; R)$ can be considered as a subgroup of the Abelian group $H^*(X; R)$, and the elements of $H^n(X; R)$ are called the n-dimensional *homogeneous elements* of the group $H^*(X; R)$. It follows from the definition of the direct sum that every element ξ of $H^*(X; R)$ can be written as the sum

$$\xi = \sum_{i=1}^{m} \xi_i$$

of a finite number of homogeneous elements $\xi_1, \ldots, \xi_m$ of different dimensions. The nonzero ones of these homogeneous elements $\xi_1, \ldots, \xi_m$ are uniquely determined by the element ξ. Hence we can define a binary operation

$$\smile \ : H^*(X; R) \times H^*(X; R) \to H^*(X; R)$$

in the Abelian group $H^*(X; R)$ as follows.

Let ξ and η denote arbitrary elements of $H^*(X; R)$. Express these as sums of homogeneous elements of different dimensions, say,

$$\xi = \sum_{i=1}^{m} \xi_i, \qquad \eta = \sum_{j=1}^{m} \eta_j.$$

Then we define $\smile$ by taking

$$\xi \smile \eta = \smile (\xi, \eta) = \sum_{i=1}^{m} \sum_{j=1}^{n} \xi_i \smile \eta_j.$$

Because of (4.2), $\smile$ is associative and hence makes $H^*(X; R)$ a semigroup. Furthermore, since

$$\smile \ : H^p(X; R) \otimes H^q(X; R) \to H^{p+q}(X; R)$$

is a homomorphism for every $p \geqslant 0$ and every $q \geqslant 0$, it follows that $\smile$ satisfies the *distributive law* in [H2, p. 114]. Hence $\smile$ makes the Abelian group $H^*(X; R)$ a ring which is called the *singular cohomology ring* of the topological space X over the coefficient ring R.

The cohomology ring $H^*(X; R)$ over a commutative ring R is, in general, not commutative but is governed by the *commutation rule* (4.3).

The construction of cup products given above was introduced by Lefschetz. We shall now establish the equivalence of this approach to the original Alexander-Whitney approach.

For this purpose, we observe that the cup product homomorphism

$$\smile \ : H^p(X; F) \otimes H^q(X; G) \to H^{p+q}(X; K)$$

defined above is the composition

$$\smile = \omega^* \circ d^* \circ h^* \circ \mu^* \circ \rho^*$$

of the following five homomorphisms:

$$\rho^*: H^p(X; F) \otimes H^p(X; G) \to H^{p+q}[C^*(X; F) \otimes C^*(X; G)],$$

$$\mu^*: H^{p+q}[C^*(X; F) \otimes C^*(X; G)] \to H^{p+q}[C(X) \otimes C(X); F \otimes G],$$

$$h^*: H^{p+q}[C(X) \otimes C(X); F \otimes G] \to H^{p+q}(X \times X; F \otimes G),$$

$$d^*\colon H^{p+q}(X \times X; F \otimes G) \to H^{p+q}(X; F \otimes G),$$

$$\omega^*\colon H^{p+q}(X; F \otimes G) \to H^{p+q}(X; K).$$

The homomorphism h^* is induced by any functorial chain homomorphism

$$h\colon C(X \times X) \to C(X) \otimes C(X)$$

in (1.2). The homomorphism d^* is induced by the chain homomorphism

$$d_\#\colon C(X) \to C(X \times X),$$

which is functorial and is induced by the diagonal imbedding $d\colon X \to X \times X$. Hence the composed homomorphism $d^* \circ h^*$ is induced by the functorial chain homomorphism

$$\beta = h \circ d_\#\colon C(X) \to C(X) \otimes C(X).$$

This chain homomorphism β has the property that

$$\beta(\sigma) = \sigma \otimes \sigma$$

for every zero-dimensional singular simplex σ in X. Every functorial chain homomorphism from $C(X)$ into $C(X) \otimes C(X)$ with this property is called a *diagonal approximation*. As in (1.4), one can easily prove that any two diagonal approximations are functorially chain homotopic. Hence, in defining cup products, β may be replaced by any other diagonal approximation.

In particular, β may be replaced by the following diagonal approximation

$$\alpha\colon C(X) \to C(X) \otimes C(X),$$

which is known as the *Alexander-Whitney approximation* and is defined as follows. For every $p \geq 0$ and every $q \geq 0$, consider the imbedding

$$i_p\colon \Delta_p \to \Delta_{p+q}$$

defined by

$$i_p(t_0, \ldots, t_p) = (t_0, \ldots, t_p, 0, \ldots, 0)$$

for every point $(t_0, \ldots, t_p)$ of Δ_p and the imbedding

$$j_q\colon \Delta_q \to \Delta_{p+q}$$

defined by

$$j_q(t_0, \ldots, t_q) = (0, \ldots, 0, t_0, \ldots, t_q)$$

for every point $(t_0, \ldots, t_q)$ of Δ_q. Then α is determined by taking

$$\alpha(\sigma) = \sum_{p+q=n} (\sigma \circ i_p) \otimes (\sigma \circ j_q)$$

for every integer $n \geqslant 0$ and every n-dimensional singular simplex σ: $\Delta_n \to X$. It is straightforward to verify that α is a diagonal approximation.

Since α and β are chain homotopic, we have

$$\alpha^* = \beta^* = d^* \circ h^*.$$

Hence we obtain the following proposition.

Proposition 4.4. *For every $p \geqslant 0$ and every $q \geqslant 0$, we have*

$$\smile = \omega^* \circ \alpha^* \circ \mu^* \circ \rho^* : H^p(X; F) \otimes H^q(X; G) \to H^{p+q}(X; K).$$

This proposition implies the equivalence of Lefschetz's definition of cup products given above to the original definition of Alexander-Whitney, described as follows.

For every $\phi \in C^p(X; F)$ and every $\psi \in C^q(X; G)$, define a cochain

$$\phi \smile \psi : C_{p+q}(X) \to K$$

by taking

$$(\phi \smile \psi)(\sigma) = \omega[\phi(\sigma \circ i_p) \otimes \psi(\sigma \circ j_q)] \in K$$

for every $(p + q)$-dimensional singular simplex $\sigma : \Delta_{p+q} \to X$. This cochain $\phi \smile \psi$ is called the *cup product* of ϕ and ψ. The assignment $\phi \otimes \psi \to \phi \smile \psi$ determines a homomorphism

$$\smile : C^p(X; F) \otimes C^q(X; G) \to C^{p+q}(X; K).$$

The following lemma can be easily verified.

Lemma 4.5. *For every $\phi \in C^p(X; F)$ and every $\psi \in C^q(X; G)$, we have*

$$\delta(\phi \smile \psi) = (\delta\phi) \smile \psi + (-1)^p \phi \smile (\delta\psi).$$

The following two corollaries are immediate consequences of (4.5).

Corollary 4.6. *For every $\phi \in Z^p(X; F)$ and every $\psi \in Z^q(X; G)$, we have*

$$\phi \smile \psi \in Z^{p+q}(X; K).$$

Corollary 4.7. $\phi \smile \psi \in B^{p+q}(X; K)$ *if at least one of the following two conditions is satisfied*:

(a) $\phi \in Z^p(X; F)$ *and* $\psi \in B^q(X; G)$.

(b) $\phi \in B^p(X; F)$ *and* $\psi \in Z^p(X; G)$.

Now let $\xi \in H^p(X; F)$ and $\eta \in H^q(X; G)$ be arbitrarily given. By definition, ξ and η are cosets of $B^p(X; F)$ and $B^q(X; G)$ in the groups $Z^p(X; F)$ and $Z^q(X; G)$, respectively. Let

$$\phi \in \xi \subset Z^p(X; F),$$

$$\psi \in \eta \subset Z^q(X; G).$$

According to (4.6), $\phi \smile \psi \in Z^{p+q}(X; K)$. From (4.7), it follows that the element ζ of $H^{p+q}(X; K)$ which contains $\phi \smile \psi$ does not depend on the choice of ϕ and ψ from the cosets ξ and η, respectively. Consequently, ζ is completely determined by the given elements ξ and η. By (4.4), this uniquely determined element ζ of $H^{p+q}(X; K)$ is the cup product of ξ and η; in symbols, we have

$$\zeta = \xi \smile \eta.$$

This completes our description of the Alexander-Whitney approach to cup products and its equivalence with the Lefschetz approach.

EXERCISES
4A. Let R denote any commutative ring in the sense of [H2, p. 114]. Prove the following assertions:
   (a) For every integer n, $H^n(X; R)$ is a module over R in the sense of [H2, p. 145].
   (b) $H^*(X; R)$ is an algebra over R in the sense of [H2, p. 147]. Hence $H^*(X; R)$ is called the *singular cohomology algebra* of X over R.
   (c) $H^0(X; R)$ is a subalgebra of $H^*(X; R)$.
   (d) The image $\epsilon(R)$ of the augmentation $\epsilon: R \to H^0(X; R)$ in Exercise 2C of Chap. 2 a subalgebra of $H^0(X; R)$.
   (e) For every $a \in R$ and every $\xi \in H^*(X; R)$, we have

$$\epsilon(a) \smile \xi = a\xi = \xi \smile \epsilon(a).$$

   (f) If R has a multiplicative unit u, then $\epsilon(u)$ is a multiplicative unit of $H^*(X; R)$; that is,

$$\epsilon(u) \smile \xi = \xi = \xi \smile \epsilon(u)$$

holds for every $\xi \in H^*(X; R)$.

4B. Let $(X; A, B)$ denote any topological triad which is proper in the sense of [H5, p. 88]. Generalize the cup product homomorphism $\smile$ in the text to a homomorphism

$$\smile : H^p(X, A; F) \otimes H^q(X, B; G) \to H^{p+q}(X, A \smile B; K)$$

for every $p \geqslant 0$ and every $q \geqslant 0$. For every $\xi \in H^p(X, A; F)$ and every $\eta \in H^q(X, B; G)$, the element

$$\xi \smile \eta = \smile (\xi, \eta)$$

of $H^{p+q}(X, A \cup B; K)$ is called the *cup product* of ξ and η. Generalize propositions (4.1) through (4.3) to this case.

4C. By applying Exercise 4B to the special case where $A = B$, show that the cup product homomorphism

$$\smile : H^p(X, A; F) \otimes H^q(X, A; G) \to H^{p+q}(X, A; K)$$

is defined for every topological pair (X, A). Hence, for every commutative ring R, the direct sum

$$H^*(X, A; R) = \sum_{n=0}^{\infty} H^n(X, A; R)$$

becomes an algebra over R under the cup product.

4D. Let (X, A) and (Y, B) denote any two topological pairs such that

$$(X \times Y; A \times Y, X \times B)$$

is a proper triad in the sense of [H5, p. 88]. Let

$$f: (X \times Y, A \times Y) \to (X, A),$$

$$g: (X \times Y, X \times B) \to (Y, B)$$

denote the natural projections. Prove that, for every $\xi \in H^p(X, A; F)$ and every $\eta \in H^q(Y, B; G)$, we have

$$\xi \times \eta = f^*(\xi) \smile g^*(\eta)$$

in the group $H^{p+q}(X \times Y, C; F \otimes G)$, where

$$C = (A \times Y) \cup (X \times B).$$

5. Cap Products

Throughout the present section, let X denote any topological space and consider an arbitrary pairing

$$\omega: F \otimes G \to K.$$

Our objective is the construction of a functorial homomorphism

$$\frown : H_n(X; F) \otimes H^q(X; G) \to H_{n-q}(X; K)$$

for every integer $n \geq 0$ and every integer q satisfying $0 \leq q \leq n$.
  For this purpose, let $p = n - q$. Then we have

$$p \geq 0, \qquad n = p + q.$$

Consider the singular chain complexes $C(X; F)$ and $C(X; K)$ together
with the singular cochain complex $C^*(X; G)$ as defined in Sec. 2, Chap. 2.
Since

$$C_n(X; F) = C_n(X) \otimes F,$$

$$C^q(X; G) = \text{Hom}[C_q(X), G],$$

we may define a homomorphism

$$\frown: C_n(X; F) \otimes C^q(X; G) \to C_p(X; K)$$

by taking

$$\frown [(\sigma \otimes f) \otimes \phi] = (\sigma \circ i_p) \otimes \omega[f \otimes \phi(\sigma \circ j_q)] \in C_p(X; K)$$

for every n-dimensional singular simplex $\sigma: \Delta_n \to X$, every $f \in F$, and
every $\phi \in C^q(X; G)$. Here,

$$i_p: \Delta_p \to \Delta_n, \qquad j_q: \Delta_q \to \Delta_n$$

denote the imbeddings defined in the preceding section.
  For every $c \in C_n(X; F)$ and every $\phi \in C^q(X; G)$, the element

$$c \frown \phi = \frown (c \otimes \phi) \in C_p(X; K)$$

is called the *cap product* of the chain c and the cochain ϕ with respect
to the pairing ω.
  The following lemma can be easily verified.

Lemma 5.1. *For every $c \in C_n(X; F)$ and every $\phi \in C^q(X; G)$, we have*

$$\partial(c \frown \phi) = (\partial c) \frown \phi + (-1)^p c \frown (\delta\phi).$$

The following two corollaries are immediate consequences of (5.1).

Corollary 5.2. *For every $c \in Z_n(X; F)$ and every $\phi \in Z^q(X; G)$,
we have*

$$c \frown \phi \in Z_p(X; K).$$

Corollary 5.3. $c \frown \phi \in B_p(X; K)$ *if at least one of the following two conditions is satisfied*:

(a) $c \in Z_n(X; F)$ *and* $\phi \in B^q(X; G)$.

(b) $c \in B_n(X; F)$ *and* $\phi \in Z^q(X; G)$.

Now let $\xi \in H_n(X; F)$ and $\eta \in H^q(X; G)$ be arbitrarily given. By definition ξ and η are cosets of $B_n(X; F)$ and $B^q(X; G)$ in the groups $Z_n(X; F)$ and $Z^q(X; G)$, respectively. Let

$$c \in \xi \subset Z_n(X; F),$$

$$\phi \in \eta \subset Z^q(X; G).$$

According to (5.2), $c \frown \phi \in Z_p(X; K)$. From (5.3), it follows that the element ζ of $H_p(X; K)$ which contains $c \frown \phi$ does not depend on the choice of c and ϕ from the cosets ξ and η, respectively. Consequently, ζ is completely determined by the given elements ξ and η. This uniquely determined element ζ of $H_p(X; K)$ is known as the *cap product* of ξ and η and will be denoted by

$$\zeta = \xi \frown \eta.$$

This assignment $\xi \otimes \eta \to \xi \frown \eta$ determines a homomorphism

$$\frown : H_n(X; F) \otimes H^q(X; G) \to H_{n-q}(X; K).$$

This completes the construction of cap products.

The following proposition can be easily verified.

Proposition 5.4. *For every map* $f: X \to Y$, *every* $\xi \in H_n(X; F)$, *and every* $\eta \in H^q(Y; G)$, *we have*

$$f_*[\xi \frown f^*(\eta)] = f_*(\xi) \frown \eta$$

in the group $H_{n-q}(Y; K)$.

For the important special case where R is a commutative ring with the pairing

$$\omega: R \otimes R \to R$$

as given in example (d) of the preceding section, we have the following proposition, which can be easily verified.

Proposition 5.5. *For arbitrary elements*

$$\xi \in H_n(X; R), \qquad \eta \in H^q(X; R), \qquad \zeta \in H^r(X; R)$$

with $q \geqslant 0$, $r \geqslant 0$, and $0 \leqslant q + r \leqslant n$, we have

$$(\xi \frown \eta) \frown \zeta = \xi \frown (\eta \frown \zeta).$$

EXERCISES

5A. Let R denote any commutative ring. Prove the following assertions:

  (a) For every integer n, $H_n(X; R)$ is a module over R in the sense of [H2, p. 145].

  (b) For every $\xi \in H_n(X; R)$ and every $a \in R$, we have

$$\xi \frown \epsilon(a) = a\,\xi$$

  where $\epsilon: R \to H^0(X; R)$ is the augmentation in Exercise 2C, Chap. 2.

  (c) If u is a multiplicative unit of R, then we have

$$\xi \frown \epsilon(u) = \xi$$

  for every $\xi \in H_n(X; R)$.

5B. Let $(X; A, B)$ denote any topological triad which is proper in the sense of [H5, p. 88]. Generalize the cap product homomorphism in the text to a homomorphism

$$\frown: H_n(X, A \smile B; F) \otimes H^q(X, A; G) \to H_{n-q}(X, B; K)$$

for every $n \geqslant 0$ and every integer q satisfying $0 \leqslant q \leqslant n$. Generalize propositions (5.4) and (5.5).

Chapter 5

DUALITY THEOREMS

This FINAL CHAPTER is devoted to a leisurely detailed exposition of the duality theorems. The first three sections cover the generalities as well as preliminary materials. The Alexander duality theorem is given in Sec. 4 and the Poincaré duality theorem is given in Sec. 5. Since the Lefschetz duality theorem is not as fundamental as the two mentioned above, it is formulated as exercises in Sec. 5. Unless explicitly stated as in the Alexander duality theorem (4.10), we shall use singular homology and singular cohomology throughout the chapter.

1. Topological Manifolds

Let n denote any given positive integer. By an *n-dimensional topological manifold*, we mean a nonempty paracompact Hausdorff space X such that every point x of X has an open neighborhood U in X which is homeomorphic to the n-dimensional Euclidean space R^n. Such a neighborhood U of x will be referred to as a *coordinate neighborhood*. Hereafter, n-dimensional topological manifolds will be simply called n-manifolds.

For example, the n-dimensional Euclidean space R^n and the n-dimensional sphere S^n are n-manifolds. Every nonempty open subspace of an n-manifold is an n-manifold. The topological sum of disjoint n-manifolds is an n-manifold. The topological product of an m-manifold and an n-manifold is an $(m + n)$-manifold.

Throughout the remainder of the present section, let X denote an arbitrarily given n-manifold.

Proposition 1.1. *For any point x of an n-manifold X, the integral singular cohomology groups of the pair $(X, X \setminus x)$ are as follows:*

$$H^q(X, X \setminus x) \approx \begin{cases} Z & \text{(if } q = n), \\ 0 & \text{(if } q \neq n). \end{cases}$$

Proof. According to the definition, there exists a coordinate neighborhood U of x in X together with a homeomorphism

$$h: U \to R^n.$$

Consider the unit ball B in R^n defined by

$$B = \{t \in R^n \mid \|t\| \leq 1\}.$$

Then the inverse image $V = h^{-1}(B)$ in U is a closed neighborhood of x in X. By (4.6) in Chap. 1, the inclusion map

$$e: (V, V \setminus x) \to (X, X \setminus x),$$

obtained by the excision of the open set $X \setminus V$ of X, induces an isomorphism

$$e^*: H^q(X, X \setminus x) \approx H^q(V, V \setminus x)$$

for every integer q.

Since $h \mid (V, V \setminus x)$ is a homeomorphism of $(V, V \setminus x)$ onto $(B, B \setminus 0)$, we have an isomorphism

$$h^*: H^q(B, B \setminus 0) \approx H^q(V, V \setminus x)$$

for every integer q.

Since B is contractible, it follows from the exact reduced cohomology sequence of the pair $(B, B \setminus 0)$ in Sec. 2, Chap. 1, that we have an isomorphism

$$\delta: \tilde{H}^{q-1}(B \setminus 0) \approx H^q(B, B \setminus 0)$$

for every integer q.

Finally, since the unit sphere S^{n-1} in R^n is a deformation retract of $B \setminus 0$, we have

$$\tilde{H}^{q-1}(B \setminus 0) \approx \tilde{H}^{q-1}(S^{n-1}) \approx \begin{cases} Z & \text{(if } q = n), \\ 0 & \text{(if } q \neq n). \end{cases}$$

This completes the proof of (1.1). ‖

Since $H^n(X, X \setminus x) \approx Z$, there are two possible elements of $H^n(X, X \setminus x)$ which can generate this infinite cyclic group. By a *local orientation* of an n-manifold X at a point $x \in X$, we mean a generator of the group $H^n(X, X \setminus x)$. Hence, at every point x of an n-manifold X, there are two local orientations. If e_x is one of the local orientations of X at x, then the other local orientation is $-e_x$.

To define a notion of an orientation of an n-manifold X globally, we have to select a local orientation e_x at each point $x \in X$ such that these local orientations "match up" in some uniform way.

For this purpose, let us consider the diagonal $d(X)$ of the topological square.

$$X^2 = X \times X$$

defined by

$$d(X) = \{(x, y) \in X^2 \mid x = y\}.$$

In fact, $d(X)$ is the image of the diagonal imbedding

$$d: X \to X^2$$

used in Sec. 3, Chap. 4

For every point $x \in X$, imbed the pair $(X, X \setminus x)$ in the pair $[X^2, X^2 \setminus d(X)]$ by means of the imbedding

$$j_x: (X, X \setminus x) \to [X^2, X^2 \setminus d(X)]$$

defined by $j_x(y) = (x, y) \in X^2$ for every point y of X. This imbedding j_x induces a homomorphism

$$j_x^*: H^n[X^2, X^2 \setminus d(X)] \to H^n(X, X \setminus x).$$

An n-manifold X is said to be *orientable* iff there exists an element

$$u \in H^n[X^2, X^2 \setminus d(X)]$$

such that $j_x^*(u)$ is a generator of $H^n(X, X \setminus x)$ for every $x \in X$. If X is orientable, then every element u of $H^n[X^2, X^2 \setminus d(X)]$ which satisfies this condition is called an *orientation* of X. Hence, an orientation u of X determines a local orientation $j_x^*(u)$ at every point x of X.

Proposition 1.2.   *The n-dimensional Euclidean space R^n is orientable.*
Proof. Let X denote R^n and let 0 denote the origin of R^n. Consider the map

$$f: [X^2, X^2 \setminus d(X)] \to (X, X \setminus 0)$$

defined by $f(x, y) = y - x$ for every point (x, y) of X^2. This map f induces a homomorphism

$$f^*: H^n(X, X \setminus 0) \to H^n[X^2, X^2 \setminus d(X)].$$

Since $H^n(X, X \setminus 0)$ is infinite cyclic, it is generated by an element e. Let

$$u = f^*(e) \in H^n[X^2, X^2 \setminus d(X)].$$

It remains to prove that u is an orientation of X.

For this purpose, observe that the composition

$$h_x = f \circ j_x: (X, X \setminus x) \to (X, X \setminus 0)$$

is a homeomorphism and hence induces an isomorphism

$$h_x^*: H^n(X, X \setminus 0) \approx H^n(X, X \setminus x).$$

This implies that $h_x^*(e)$ is a generator of $H^n(X, X \setminus x)$. Since

$$j_x^*(u) = j_x^*[f^*(e)] = h_x^*(e),$$

$j_x^*(u)$ is a generator of $H^n(X, X \setminus x)$ for every $x \in X$. This proves that u is an orientation of $X = R^n$. ∥

EXERCISES

1A. Prove that, for every orientation u of an orientable n-manifold X, $-u$ is also an orientation of X.

1B. Prove that every point x of an n-manifold X has an open neighborhood V such that $[V \times X, (V \times X) \setminus d(V)]$ is homeomorphic to $[V \times X, V \times (X \setminus x)]$ by a homeomorphism which preserves the first coordinates [Sp, p. 293].

1C. Let u and v denote any two orientations of a connected orientable n-manifold X, and let x be an arbitrarily given point in X. Prove that $u = v$ iff $j_x^*(u) = j_x^*(v)$. Hence deduce that every connected orientable n-manifold X has exactly two orientations.

1D. Prove that every simply connected n-manifold is orientable.

2. Slant Products

Throughout the present section, let

$$\omega: F \otimes G \to K$$

denote an arbitrarily given pairing of two Abelian groups F, G into an Abelian group K.

Let X and Y denote arbitrary topological spaces. For any two integers n and q, we shall define a homomorphism

$$h: C^n[C(X) \otimes C(Y); F] \otimes C_q(Y; G) \to C^{n-q}(X; K)$$

as follows. We may assume $0 \le q \le n$, for otherwise h must be the trivial homomorphism.

Let $\phi \in C^n[C(X) \otimes C(Y); F]$ and $e \in C_q(Y; G)$ be arbitrarily given. By definition, ϕ is a homomorphism

$$\phi: T_n(X, Y) \to F$$

of the group

$$T_n(X, Y) = \sum_{i=0}^{n} C_i(X) \otimes C_{n-i}(Y)$$

in Sec. 1, Chap. 4. On the other hand, e can be uniquely expressed as a finite sum

$$e = \sum_{j=1}^{m} \sigma_j \otimes g_j,$$

where $\sigma_j: \Delta_q \to Y$ is a singular q-simplex in Y and g_j is an element in G. Then we define an element

$$h(\phi, e) \in C^{n-q}(X; K)$$

by taking

$$[h(\phi, e)](c) = \sum_{j=1}^{m} \omega[\phi(c \otimes \sigma_j) \otimes g_j]$$

for every $c \in C_{n-q}(X)$. This completes the definition of the homomorphism h.

The following lemma can be easily verified.

Lemma 2.1. *For every* $\phi \in C^n[C(X) \otimes C(Y); F]$ *and every* $e \in C_q(Y; G)$, *we have*

$$\delta[h(\phi, e)] = h[\delta(\phi), e] + (-1)^{n-q} h[\phi, \partial(e)].$$

The following two corollaries are immediate consequences of (2.1).

Corollary 2.2. *For every* $\phi \in Z^n[C(X) \otimes C(Y); F]$ *and every* $e \in Z_q(Y; G)$, *we have*

$$h(\phi, e) \in Z^{n-q}(X; K).$$

Corollary 2.3. $h(\phi, e) \in B^{n-q}(X; K)$ *if at least one of the following two conditions is satisfied:*

(a) $\phi \in Z^n[C(X) \otimes C(Y); F]$ *and* $e \in B_q(Y; G)$.

(b) $\phi \in B^n[C(X) \otimes C(Y); F]$ *and* $e \in Z_q(Y; G)$.

Because of (2.2) and (2.3), the homomorphism h induces a homomorphism

$$h^*: H^n[C(X) \otimes C(Y); F] \otimes H_q(Y; G) \to H^{n-q}(X; K)$$

for any two integers n and q.

On the other hand, let us consider any functorial chain homomorphism

$$k: C(X) \otimes C(Y) \to C(X \times Y)$$

as described in (1.3), Chap. 4. Thic chain homomorphism k induces a homomorphism

$$k^*: H^n(X \times Y; F) \to H^n[C(X) \otimes C(Y); F]$$

which does not depend on the particular choice of the chain homomorphism k.

Consequently, we may define a homomorphism

$$\theta: H^n(X \times Y; F) \otimes H_q(Y; G) \to H^{n-q}(X; K)$$

by taking

$$\theta(\xi \otimes \eta) = h^*[k^*(\xi) \otimes \eta]$$

for every $\xi \in H^n(X \times Y; F)$ and every $\eta \in H_q(Y; G)$.

For every $\xi \in H^n(X \times Y; F)$ and every $\eta \in H_q(Y; G)$, the element

$$\xi/\eta = \theta(\xi \otimes \eta) \in H^{n-q}(X; K)$$

is known as the *slant product* of ξ and η with respect to the pairing ω [Sp, pp. 286–292].

Because of the application in the sequel, we must consider the generalization of slant products to relative groups.

For this purpose, let us consider any two topological pairs (X, A) and (Y, B). By the *topological product*

$$(X, A) \times (Y, B)$$

of (X, A) and (Y, B), we mean the pair (Z, C) with

$$Z = X \times Y, \qquad C = (A \times Y) \cup (X \times B).$$

Since the chain homomorphism $k\colon C(X) \otimes C(Y) \to C(X \times Y)$ is functorial, one can easily see that k induces a chain homomorphism

$$k\colon C(X,A) \otimes C(Y,B) \to C(Z,C).$$

This new chain homomorphism k induces a homomorphism

$$k^*\colon H^n(Z,C;F) \to H^n[C(X,A) \otimes C(Y,B);F]$$

which does not depend on the particular choice of the chain homomorphism k.

On the other hand, by replacing $C(X)$ by $C(X,A)$ and $C(Y)$ by $C(Y,B)$, the preceding construction of the homomorphism h gives a homomorphism

$$h\colon C^n[C(X,A) \otimes C(Y;B);F] \otimes C_q(Y,B;G) \to C^{n-q}(X,A;K).$$

Since (2.1) still holds in this case, h induces a homomorphism

$$h^*\colon H^n[C(X,A) \otimes C(Y,B);F] \otimes H_q(Y,B;G) \to H^{n-q}(X,A;K).$$

Consequently, we may define a homomorphism

$$\theta\colon H^n(Z,C;F) \otimes H_q(Y,B;G) \to H^{n-q}(X,A;K)$$

for any two integers n and q by taking

$$\theta(\xi \otimes \eta) = h^*[k^*(\xi) \otimes \eta]$$

for every $\xi \in H^n(Z,C;F)$ and every $\eta \in H_q(Y,B;G)$.

For every $\xi \in H^n(Z,C;F)$ and every $\eta \in H_q(Y,B;G)$, the element

$$\xi/\eta = \theta(\xi \otimes \eta) \in H^{n-q}(X,A;K)$$

is called the slant product of ξ and η with respect to the pairing ω.

Since the chain homomorphism k is functorial, one can easily verify the following proposition.

Proposition 2.4. *For arbitrary maps $f\colon (X,A) \to (X',A')$ and $g\colon (Y,B) \to (Y',B')$, we have*

$$[(f \times g)^*(\xi)]/\eta = f^*[\xi/g_*(\eta)]$$

for every $\xi \in H^n(Z',C';F)$ and every $\eta \in H_q(Y,B;G)$, where

$$(Z',C') = (X',A') \times (Y',B').$$

Now let X denote an arbitrary orientable n-manifold X with any given orientation

$$u \in H^n[X^2, X^2\backslash d(X)].$$

Consider the special pairing with $F = Z$, $K = G$, and

$$\omega: Z \otimes G \to G$$

as defined in example (b) of Sec. 4, Chap. 4.

For a pair of subspaces A and B of X with $B \subset A \subset X$, we may define a homomorphism

$$\gamma_u: H_q(X \backslash B, X \backslash A; G) \to H^{n-q}(A, B; G)$$

for every integer q as follows.

First we observe

$$A \times (X \backslash B) \subset X^2,$$

$$[A \times (X \backslash A)] \cup [B \times (X \backslash B)] \subset X^2 \backslash d(X^2),$$

and hence we obtain an inclusion map

$$i: (A, B) \times (X \backslash B, X \backslash A) \to [X^2, X^2 \backslash d(X)].$$

This inclusion map i induces a homomorphism

$$i^*: H^n[X^2, X^2 \backslash d(X)] \to H^n[(A, B) \times (X \backslash B, X \backslash A)].$$

Hence we may define γ_u by taking

$$\gamma_u(\eta) = i^*(u)/\eta \in H^{n-q}(A, B; G)$$

for every $\eta \in H_q(X \backslash B, X \backslash A; G)$.

In particular, for the case $B = \square$, we obtain a homomorphism

$$\gamma_u: H_q(X, X \backslash A; G) \to H^{n-q}(A; G)$$

for every subspace A of X and every integer q. This homomorphism will be used to establish the duality theorems in the sequel.

EXERCISES

2A. Let R denote a commutative ring with a multiplicative unit 1. Prove the following assertions:

(a) For every $u \in H^p(X; R)$, $v \in H^n(X \times Y; R)$, and $w \in H_q(Y; R)$,

$$u \smile (v/w) = [(u \times 1) \smile v]/w$$

holds in the group $H^{p+n-q}(X; R)$.

(b) For every $u \in H^n(X \times Y; R)$, $v \in H_q(Y; G)$, and $w \in H^p(Y; R)$,

$$u/(v \frown w) = [u \smile (1 \times w)]/v$$

holds in the group $H^{p+n-q}(X; R)$.

(c) For every $u \in H_p(X; R)$, $v \in H_q(X; R)$, and $w \in H^n(X \times Y; R)$,

$$\pi_*[(u \times v) \frown w] = u \frown (w/v)$$

holds in the group $H_{p+q-n}(X; R)$, where $\pi: X \times Y \to X$ denotes the natural projection.

2B. Prove that, for every $u \in H^p(X, A)$, $v \in H^q(Y, B)$, and $w \in H_q(Y, B)$, we have

$$(u \times v)/w = \chi_*(v, w)u$$

in the group $H^p(X, A)$, where χ_* denotes the homomorphism

$$\chi_*: H^q(Y, B) \otimes H_q(Y, B) \to Z$$

induced by the homomorphism

$$\chi: C^q(Y, B) \otimes C_q(Y, B) \to Z,$$

which is defined by

$$\chi(\phi, c) = \phi(c) \in Z$$

for every $\phi \in C^q(Y, B) = \mathrm{Hom}[C_q(Y, B), Z]$ and every $c \in C_q(Y, B)$.

2C. Prove that, for every orientation u of R^n and every point $x_0 \in R^n$, the homomorphism

$$\gamma_u: H_q(R^n, R^n \setminus x_0; G) \to H^{n-q}(x_0; G)$$

is an isomorphism for every integer q and every Abelian group G.

2D. Let (A, B) and (A', B') denote any two topological pairs in an n-manifold X satisfying

$$(A, B) \subset (A', B').$$

Prove that the following rectangle is commutative:

$$
\begin{array}{ccc}
H_q(X \setminus B', X \setminus A'; G) & \xrightarrow{\gamma_u} & H^{n-q}(A', B'; G) \\
\downarrow{\scriptstyle j_*} & & \downarrow{\scriptstyle i^*} \\
H_q(X \setminus B, X \setminus A; \ G) & \xrightarrow{\gamma_u} & H^{n-q}(A, B; G)
\end{array}
$$

where $i: (A, B) \to (A', B')$ and $j: (X \setminus B', X \setminus A') \to (X \setminus B, X \setminus A)$ denote the inclusion maps.

2E. Let (A, B) denote any topological pair in an n-manifold X. Prove that the rectangle

$$H_q(X, X \setminus B; G) \xrightarrow{\gamma_u} H^{n-q}(B; G)$$

$$\downarrow \partial \qquad\qquad\qquad \downarrow \delta$$

$$H_{q-1}(X \setminus B, X \setminus A; G) \xrightarrow{\gamma_u} H^{n-q+1}(A, B; G)$$

is commutative up to possibly a sign.

3. Direct Limits

Let A denote any subspace of an arbitrarily given topological space X. Consider the system

$$\mathcal{N} = \{U \subset X | A \subset \text{Int}(U)\}$$

of all neighborhoods of A in X.

Let G denote an arbitrary Abelian group and q any integer. For every $U \in \mathcal{N}$, consider the cohomology group

$$H^q(U; G).$$

For any $V \in \mathcal{N}$ satisfying $V \supset U$, the inclusion map

$$i: U \to V$$

induces a homomorphism

$$h_{(V,U)} = i^*: H^q(V; G) \to H^q(U; G).$$

For arbitrary U, V, W in $\mathcal{N}$ satisfying $W \supset V \supset U$, we obviously have

$$h_{(V,U)} \circ h_{(W,V)} = h_{(W,U)}.$$

For any two neighborhoods U and V of A in X, the intersection

$$W = U \cap V$$

is also a neighborhood of A in X and satisfies

$$U \supset W, \qquad V \supset W.$$

Because of this property, we say that the system $\mathcal{N}$ is directed by the relation $\supset$. Because of the relation

$$h_{(V,U)} \circ h_{(W,V)} = h_{(W,U)}$$

given above and because $h_{(U,U)}$ is the identity homomorphism, the system

$$\mathscr{S} = \{H^q(U; G), h_{(V,U)}\}$$

for all $U \in \mathscr{N}$ and all (V, U) with $V \supset U$ is called a *direct system* of Abelian groups.

Consider the direct sum

$$D = \sum_{U \in \mathscr{N}} H^q(U; G)$$

as defined in [H2, p. 77]. For each $U \in \mathscr{N}$, $H^q(U; G)$ is considered as a subgroup of D in the obvious way.

For any two members U, V of $\mathscr{N}$ satisfying $V \supset U$ and every $\xi \in H^q(V; G)$, the element

$$h_{(V,U)}(\xi) - \xi \in D$$

is called a *relation* in D. Let K denote the subgroup of D generated by all relations in D. The quotient group

$$D/K$$

is called the *direct limit* of the system $\mathscr{S}$ and is usually denoted by

$$\varinjlim\{H^q(U; G) | U \in \mathscr{N}\}.$$

This Abelian group D/K depends not only on the space A but also on the imbedding of A as a subspace of X. Hereafter, we shall denote this Abelian group D/K by the symbol

$$H^q_X(A; G).$$

A subset $\mathscr{M}$ of $\mathscr{N}$ is said to be *cofinal* iff, for every $U \in \mathscr{N}$, there exists a $V \in \mathscr{M}$ satisfying $U \supset V$. Every cofinal subset $\mathscr{M}$ of $\mathscr{N}$ is also directed by the relation, and hence the direct limit

$$\varinjlim \{H^q(V; G) \mid V \in \mathscr{M}\}$$

is well defined. The following proposition can be easily verified.

Proposition 3.1. *For every cofinal subset $\mathscr{M}$ of $\mathscr{N}$, the inclusion homomorphism*

$$i: \Sigma_{V \in \mathscr{M}} H^q(V; G) \to D$$

induces an isomorphism

$$i^*: \varinjlim \{H^q(V; G) \mid V \in \mathscr{M}\} \approx H^q_X(A; G).$$

For every $U \in \mathcal{N}$, the inclusion map $j_U: A \to U$ induces a homomorphism

$$j_U^*: H^q(U; G) \to H^q(A; G).$$

The following proposition can be easily verified.

Proposition 3.2. *The direct sum*

$$\Sigma_{U \in \mathcal{N}} j_U^*: D \to H^q(A; G)$$

induces a homomorphism

$$j^*: H_X^q(A; G) \to H^q(A; G).$$

A subspace A of a topological space X is said to be *taut* iff the homomorphism j^* in (3.2) is an isomorphism for every integer q and every Abelian group G.

The following proposition is an easy consequence of (3.1).

Proposition 3.3. *If A has arbitrarily small neighborhoods V in X such that the inclusion map $j_V: A \to V$ is a homotopy equivalence, then A is a taut subspace of X.*

The following corollary is a direct consequence of (3.3).

Corollary 3.4. *Every open subset A of a topological space X is a taut subspace of X.*

The following corollary is an easy consequence of (3.3) and the properties of closed ANR subspaces in ANR [H4, pp. 119–122].

Corollary 3.5. *If X is an ANR, then every closed ANR subset A of X is a taut subspace of X.*

Since every finitely triangulable space is an ANR [H4, p. 106], the following corollary is a direct consequence of (3.5).

Corollary 3.6. *If X is an ANR, then every finitely triangulable subset A of X is a taut subspace of X.*

The following corollary is an immediate consequence of (3.1) and (3.4).

Corollary 3.7. *For every integer q and every Abelian group G, we have*

$$\varinjlim \{H_X^q(U; G) \mid U \in \mathcal{N}\} \approx H_X^q(A; G).$$

EXERCISES

3A. By a *pair* (A, B) in a topological space X, we mean two subspaces A, B of X satisfying $B \subset A$. By a *neighborhood pair* of (A, B) in X, we mean a pair (U, V) in X where U is a neighborhood of A and V is a neighborhood of B. Let $\mathcal{N}$ denote the system of all neighborhood pairs of (A, B) in X. Define the direct limit

$$H_{\mathscr{X}}^{q}(A, B; G) = \varinjlim \{H^q(U, V; G) \mid (U, V) \in \mathcal{N}\}.$$

Generalize the propositions and corollaries (3.1) through (3.7) together with the related homomorphisms and necessary terminology.

3B. A pair (A, B) in a space X is said to be taut iff

$$j^*: H_{\mathscr{X}}^{q}(A, B; G) \approx H^q(A, B; G)$$

for every q and G. Prove that, if two of the three pairs $(A, \square)$, $(B, \square)$, and (A, B) are taut, so is the third.

3C. Let B and C denote closed subspaces of a space X. Establish an exact sequence

$$\cdots \to E^q \to F^q \to D^q \to E^{q+1} \to \cdots ,$$

with

$$D^q = H_{X}^{q}(B \cap C; G)$$

$$E^q = H_{X}^{q}(B \cup C; G)$$

$$F^q = H_{\mathscr{X}}^{q}(B; G) \otimes H_{\mathscr{X}}^{q}(C; G),$$

similar to the *Mayer-Vietoris sequence* in Sec. 4, Chap. 1.

3D. Let $\mathcal{N}$ denote the system of all neighborhoods of a closed subspace A in a paracompact Hausdorff space X. For Alexander cohomology groups, prove that

$$j^*: \varinjlim \{H^q(U; G) \mid U \in \mathcal{N}\} \to H^q(A; G)$$

is an isomorphism for every integer q and every Abelian group G. In other words, every closed subspace A of any paracompact Hausdorff space X is taut with respect to the Alexander cohomology theory.

3E. Establish the *weak continuity property* of the Alexander cohomology theory: For any system $\mathscr{S}$ of compact Hausdorff subspaces of a topological space X directed by $\supset$, we have

$$\varinjlim \{H^q(V; G) \mid V \in \mathscr{S}\} \approx H^q(A; G),$$

where A stands for the intersection of all subspaces V in $\mathscr{S}$.

4. Alexander Duality Theorem

In the present section, we are concerned with the n-dimensional Euclidean space R^n together with its compact subsets and their complements.

Lemma 4.1. *For any point x_0 of a subspace A of R^n which is homeomorphic to a simplex, we have*

$$H_q(R^n \setminus x_0, R^n \setminus A; G) = 0$$

for every integer q and every Abelian group G.

Proof. We may consider R^n as the complement $S^n \setminus y_0$ of the n-sphere S^n with $y_0 \in S^n$. One can easily see that the inclusion map

$$e: (R^n \setminus x_0, R^n \setminus A) \to (S^n \setminus x_0, S^n \setminus A)$$

induces an isomorphism

$$e_*: H_q(R^n \setminus x_0, R^n \setminus A; G) \approx H_q(S^n \setminus x_0, S^n \setminus A; G)$$

for every integer q and every Abelian group G.

Since $S^n \setminus x_0$ is contractible, it follows from [H5, p. 26, 4.9] that we have

$$\tilde{H}_q(S^n \setminus x_0; G) = 0$$

for every integer q and every Abelian group G. By the exactness of the reduced homology sequence [H5, p. 25], this implies

$$H_q(S^n \setminus x_0, S^n \setminus A; G) \approx \tilde{H}_{q-1}(S^n \setminus A; G)$$

for every integer q and every Abelian group G.

Finally, since A is homeomorphic to a simplex, it follows from a property of singular homology groups [Sp, p. 197] that we have

$$\tilde{H}_{q-1}(S^n \setminus A; G) = 0$$

for every integer q and every Abelian group G. This completes the proof of (4.1) ‖

According to (1.2), the n-dimensional Euclidean space R^n is an orientable n-manifold. Let

$$u \in H^n[R^n \times R^n, (R^n \times R^n) \setminus d(R^n)]$$

denote an orientation of R^n. Consider the homomorphism

$$\gamma_u: H_q(R^n, R^n \setminus A; G) \to H^{n-q}(A; G)$$

constructed at the end of Sec. 2 of this chapter, where A stands for an arbitrary subspace of R^n.

Lemma 4.2.   *If the subspace A of R^n is homeomorphic to a simplex, then the homomorphism*

$$\gamma_u: H_q(R^n, R^n \setminus A; G) \to H^{n-q}(A; G)$$

is an isomorphism for every integer q and every Abelian group G.

   Proof.   Select a point $x_0 \in A$ and let

$$D_q = H_q(R^n \setminus x_0, R^n \setminus A; G),$$

$$E_q = H_q(R^n, R^n \setminus A; G),$$

$$F_q = H_q(R^n, R^n \setminus x_0; G)$$

for every q.   Then we have the following diagram:

$$
\begin{array}{ccccccccc}
\cdots \to & D_q & \longrightarrow & E_q & \longrightarrow & F_q & \longrightarrow & D_{q-1} & \to \cdots \\
 & \downarrow{\gamma_u} & & \downarrow{\gamma_u} & & \downarrow{\gamma_u} & & \downarrow{\gamma_u} & \\
\cdots \to & H^{n-q}(A, x_0; G) & \to & H^{n-q}(A; G) & \to & H^{n-q}(x_0; G) & \to & H^{n-q+1}(A, x_0; G) & \to \cdots
\end{array}
$$

   Here, the top row is the exact singular homology sequence of the topological triple $(R^n, R^n \setminus x_0, R^n \setminus A)$ over G; the bottom row is the exact singular cohomology sequence of the topological pair (A, x_0) over G; and the vertical homomorphisms γ_u are as defined in Sec. 2.

   By Exercise 2C, the two rectangles on the left are commutative.   By Exercise 2D, the rectangle on the right is commutative up to possibly a sign.   Hence we may apply the *five lemma* [H2, p. 74] to this diagram.

   According to the five lemma, the homomorphism $\gamma_u: E_q \to H^{n-q}(A; G)$ is an isomorphism for every integer q if the homomorphisms

$$\gamma_u: D_q \to H^{n-q}(A, x_0; G), \qquad \gamma_u: F_q \to H^{n-q}(x_0; G)$$

are isomorphisms for every integer q.

   According to (4.1), we have

$$D_q = H_q(R^n \setminus x_0, R^n \setminus A; G) = 0$$

for every integer q.   Since A is contractible, it follows from (2.8), Chap. 1, that we have

$$H^{n-q}(A, x_0; G) \approx \tilde{H}^{n-q}(A; G) = 0$$

for every integer q.   Hence

$$\gamma_u: D_q \to H^{n-q}(A, x_0; G)$$

is an isomorphism for every integer q.

On the other hand, the homomorphism

$$\gamma_u: F_q \to H^{n-q}(x_0; G)$$

is also an isomorphism for every integer q according to Exercise 2C. This completes the proof of (4.2). ‖

Now let us establish the following theorem.

Theorem 4.3. *For every orientation u of R^n and every finitely triangulable subspace A of R^n, the homomorphism*

$$\gamma_u: H_q(R^n, R^n \backslash A; G) \to H^{n-q}(A; G)$$

is an isomorphism for every integer q and every Abelian group G.

Proof. If A is empty, then (4.3) is trivial. If A is homeomorphic to a single simplex, then (4.3) reduces to (4.2).

To complete the proof of (4.3) by induction, let $k > 1$ and assume that (4.3) has been proved for every finitely triangulable subspace A which is homeomorphic to a simplicial complex with less than k simplexes.

Let A denote an arbitrary subspace of R^n which is homeomorphic to a simplicial complex K with k simplexes. Let

$$h: K \to A$$

denote a homeomorphism from K onto the subspace A of R^n, and let σ denote a closed *principal simplex* of K; that is, σ is a simplex of K but is not a face of any other simplex of K. Then,

$$L = K \backslash \mathrm{Int}(\sigma)$$

is a subcomplex of K with $k - 1$ simplexes.

Let $B = h(L)$ and $C = h(\sigma)$. Then we have $A = B \cup C$. By our inductive hypothesis, we have

$$\gamma_u: H_q(R^n, R^n \backslash B; G) \approx H^{n-q}(B; G).$$

By (4.2), we have

$$\gamma_u: H_q(R^n, R^n \backslash C; G) \approx H^{n-q}(C; G).$$

For every integer q, let

$$E_q = H_q(R^n, R^n \backslash B; G) \otimes H_q(R^n, R^n \backslash C; G),$$

$$F^{n-q} = H^{n-q}(B; G) \otimes H^{n-q}(C; G),$$

and let

$$\beta_q = \gamma_u \otimes \gamma_u: E_q \approx F^{n-q}.$$

On the other hand, let

$$D = B \cap C.$$

Since D is homeomorphic to a simplicial complex with less than k simplexes, our inductive hypothesis also gives

$$\gamma_u : H_q(R^n, R^n \setminus D; G) \approx H^{n-q}(D; G)$$

for every integer q.

Consider the following diagram:

$$\cdots \to E_{q+1} \xrightarrow{\phi} H_{q+1}(R^n, R^n \setminus D; G) \xrightarrow{\Delta} H_q(R^n, R^n \setminus A; G) \xrightarrow{\psi} E_q \to \cdots$$

$$\downarrow \beta_{q+1} \qquad \downarrow \gamma_u \qquad\qquad\qquad \downarrow \gamma_u \qquad\qquad\qquad \downarrow \beta_q$$

$$\cdots \to F^{n-q-1} \xrightarrow{\psi} H^{n-q-1}(D; G) \xrightarrow{\Delta} H^{n-q}(A; G) \xrightarrow{\phi} F^{n-q} \to \cdots$$

Here, the top row is the exact relative Mayer-Vietoris sequence for homology of the proper topological triad

$$(R^n; R^n \setminus B, R^n \setminus C)$$

as given in [H5, p. 114], and the bottom row is the exact Mayer-Vietoris sequence for cohomology of the proper topological triad

$$(A; B, C)$$

as given in Sec. 4, Chap. 1.

By means of Exercise 2D, one can easily prove that the left rectangle and the right rectangle in the preceding diagram are both commutative. By means of Exercise 2E, one can also show that the central rectangle is commutative up to possibly a sign. Hence we can apply the five lemma [H2, p. 76] to the preceding diagram. Because of

$$\gamma_u : H_q(R^n, R^n \setminus D; G) \approx H^{n-q}(D; G),$$

$$\beta_q : E_q \approx F^{n-q}$$

for every integer q, it follows from the five lemma that the homomorphism

$$\gamma_u : H_q(R^n, R^n \setminus A; G) \to H^{n-q}(A; G)$$

is an isomorphism for every integer q. This completes the induction and proves (4.3). ‖

Now it is easy to establish the following theorem.

Theorem 4.4. *(Alexander Duality Theorem for Finitely Triangulable Subspaces of R^n). For every finitely triangulable subspace A of the* *n-dimensional Eculidean space R^n and any Abelian group G, we have*

$$\tilde{H}_q(R^n\backslash A; G) \approx H^{n-q-1}(A; G)$$

for every integer q.

Here $\tilde{H}_q(R^n\backslash A; G)$ stands for the q-dimensional reduced singular homology group of $R^n\backslash A$ over G as defined in [H5, p. 22].

Proof. Since R^n is contractible, it follows from [H5, p. 26, (4.10)] that the boundary homomorphism

$$\partial: H_{q+1}(R^n, R^n\backslash A; G) \to \tilde{H}_q(R^n\backslash A; G)$$

is an isomorphism for every integer q. On the other hand, (4.3) gives an isomorphism

$$\gamma_u: H_{q+1}(R^n, R^n\backslash A; G) \to H^{n-q-1}(A; G)$$

for every integer q. Hence we obtain an isomorphism

$$\theta_q = \gamma_u \circ \partial^{-1}: \tilde{H}_q(R^n\backslash A; G) \approx H^{n-q-1}(A; G)$$

for every integer q. This completes the proof of (4.4). ‖

Applying (4.4) to spheres in the n-dimensional Euclidean space R^n, we obtain the following corollary.

Corollary 4.5. *If a subspace A of the n-dimensional Euclidean space R^n is homeomorphic to an m-sphere, then its residual space $R^n\backslash A$ is a homology $(n - m - 1)$-sphere; that is,*

$$H_q(R^n\backslash A; G) \approx H_q(S^{n-m-1}; G)$$

holds for every integer q and every Abelian group G.

In particular, if $m = n - 1$, then we have $n - m - 1 = 0$. Hence we obtain the following corollary.

Corollary 4.6. *If a subspace A of the n-dimensional Euclidean space R^n is homeomorphic to an $(n - 1)$-sphere, then its residual space $R^n\backslash A$ consists of two components. Furthermore, one and only one of the two components of $R^n\backslash A$ is bounded.*

Proof. According to (4.5), we have the integral singular homology group

$$H_0(R^n\backslash A) \approx H_0(S^0) \approx Z \oplus Z.$$

Since $H_0(R^n\backslash A)$ is isomorphic to the free Abelian group $F[\pi_0(R^n\backslash A)]$ generated by the set $\pi_0\backslash(R^n\backslash A)$ of all path components of the space $R^n\backslash A$ [H5, p. 214, (3.2)], this implies that $R^n\backslash A$ consists of two path components.

As a compact subset of R^n, A is bounded. Hence there exists a positive real number r such that

$$\|x\| < r$$

holds for every point $x \in A$. Since the subset

$$W = \{x \in R^n | \ \|x\| \geq r\}$$

of $R^n \backslash A$ is pathwise connected, it must be contained in one of the two path components of $R^n \backslash A$. Hence one and only one of the two path components of $R^n \backslash A$ is bounded.

As an open subspace of a locally pathwise connected space R^n, $R^n \backslash A$ is locally pathwise connected. This implies that the path components of $R^n \backslash A$ coincide with the components of $R^n \backslash A$. Thus the proof of (4.6) is complete. ‖

By a *simple closed curve* in a topological space X, we mean a subspace A of X which is homeomorphic to the 1-sphere S^1. Then the following corollary is a special case of (4.6).

Corollary 4.7 *(Jordan Curve Theorem). If A is a simple closed curve in the Euclidean plane R^2, then $R^2 \backslash A$ consists of two components. Furthermore, one and only one of the two components of $R^2 \backslash A$ is bounded.*

The remainder of the present section is devoted to generalizing (4.4) to compact subspaces of R^n.

Lemma 4.8. *For every compact subspace A of R^n, we have an isomorphism*

$$H_q(R^n, R^n \backslash A; G) \approx H^{n-q}_{R^n}(A; G)$$

for every integer q and every Abelian group G.

Proof. Let $\mathcal{M}$ denote the set of all finitely triangulable neighborhoods of A in R^n. Then $\mathcal{M}$ is a cofinal subset of the set $\mathcal{N}$ of all neighborhoods of A in R^n. According to (3.1), we have an isomorphism

$$\lim_{\rightarrow} \{H^{n-q}(V; G) \mid V \in \mathcal{M}\} \approx H^{n-q}_{R^n}(A; G)$$

for every integer q and every Abelian group G.

For every $V \in \mathcal{M}$, it follows from (4.3) that we have an isomorphism

$$\gamma_u : H_q(R^n, R^n \backslash V; G) \approx H^{n-q}(V; G)$$

for every integer q and every Abelian group G. Because of Exercise

2D and the preceding paragraph, this implies that

$$\lim_{\rightarrow} \{H_q(R^n, R^n \backslash V; G) \mid V \in \mathcal{M}\} \approx H^{n-q}_{R^n}(A; G)$$

for every integer q and every Abelian group G.

Since A is the intersection of all $V \in \mathcal{M}$, we have

$$R^n \backslash A = \cup_{V \in \mathcal{M}} (R^n \backslash V).$$

By means of this and the compactness of Δ_q, one can show

$$\lim_{\rightarrow} \{H_q(R^n, R^n \backslash V; G) \mid V \in \mathcal{M}\} \approx H_q(R^n, R^n \backslash A; G).$$

Combining this with the isomorphism in the preceding paragraph, we obtain

$$H_q(R^n, R^n \backslash A; G) \approx H^{n-q}_{R^n}(A; G)$$

for every integer q and every Abelian group G. ‖

Lemma 4.9. *The group*

$$H^{n-q}_{R^n}(A; G)$$

in (4.8) is isomorphic to the $(n-q)$-dimensional Alexander cohomology group of A over G.

Proof. Consider the system $\mathcal{M}$ of all finitely triangulable neighborhoods of A in R^n. In the proof of (4.8), we obtained

$$\lim_{\rightarrow} \{H^{n-q}(V; G) \mid V \in \mathcal{M}\} \approx H^{n-q}_{R^n}(A; G).$$

On the other hand, since every $V \in \mathcal{M}$ is finitely triangulable, it follows from the uniqueness theorem (Chap. I, 3.8) that we may consider $H^{n-q}(V; G)$ as the $(n-q)$-dimensional Alexander cohomology group of V over G. Since every $V \in \mathcal{M}$ is a compact Hausdorff subspace of R^n and A is the intersection of all $V \in \mathcal{M}$, we may apply the weak continuity property of the Alexander cohomology theory in Exercise 3E to this case and obtain an isomorphism

$$\lim_{\rightarrow} \{H^{n-q}(V; G) \mid V \in \mathcal{M}\} \approx H^{n-q}(A; G),$$

where $H^{n-q}(A; G)$ denotes the $(n-q)$-dimensional Alexander cohomology group of A over G.

Combining the isomorphisms in the preceding two paragraphs, we obtain (4.9). ‖

The following generalization of (4.4) is an easy consequence of (4.8) and (4.9), as in the proof of (4.4).

Theorem 4.10 (*Alexander Duality Theorem for Compact Subspaces of R^n*). *If we use reduced singular homology and Alexander cohomology, then we have*

$$\tilde{H}_q(R^n \backslash A; G) \approx H^{n-q-1}(A; G)$$

for every compact subspace A of R^n, every Abelian group G, and every integer q.

EXERCISES

4A. Establish the following generalization of (4.3): For every orientation u of R^n and every finitely triangulable pair (A, B) in R^n, the homomorphism

$$\gamma_u: H_q(R^n \backslash B, R^n \backslash A; G) \to H^{n-q}(A, B; G)$$

is an isomorphism for every integer q and every Abelian group G.

4B. Establish the *relative Alexander duality theorem*: If we use singular homology and Alexander cohomology, then we have

$$H_q(R^n \backslash B, R^n \backslash A; G) \approx H^{n-q}(A, B; G)$$

for every compact pair (A, B) in R^n, every Abelian group G, and every integer q.

5. Poincaré Duality Theorem

Throughout the present section, let X denote an arbitrary n-manifold and A any compact subspace of X. Select an arbitrary orientation

$$u \in H^n[X^2, X^2 \backslash d(X)].$$

Consider the system $\mathcal{N}$ of all neighborhoods of A in X. For every $V \in \mathcal{N}$, consider the homomorphism

$$\gamma_u: H_q(X, X \backslash V; G) \to H^{n-q}(V; G)$$

constructed in Sec. 2. As in the proof of (4.8), we may identify the direct limit

$$\lim_{\rightarrow}\{H_q(X, X \backslash V; G) | V \in \mathcal{N}\}$$

with the singular homology group

$$H_q(X, X \backslash A; G).$$

On the other hand, we have

$$\lim_{\rightarrow}\{H^{n-q}(V; G)|V \in \mathcal{N}\} = H_X^{n-q}(A; G)$$

according to the definition in Sec. 3. Hence the homomorphisms γ_u for all $V \in \mathcal{N}$ induce a homomorphism

$$\beta_u: H_q(X, X \backslash A; G) \rightarrow H_X^{n-q}(A; G)$$

for every integer q and every Abelian group G.

One can easily see that this homomorphism β_u coincides with the isomorphism constructed in the proof of (4.8) whenever $X = R^n$. Hence we have the following lemma.

Lemma 5.1. *If $X = R^n$, then the homomorphism*

$$\beta_u: H_q(X, X \backslash A; G) \rightarrow H_X^{n-q}(A; G)$$

is an isomorphism for every integer q and every Abelian group G.

Now let us establish the following lemma.

Lemma 5.2. *If A is contained in a coordinate neighborhood of X, then the homomorphism*

$$\beta_u: H_q(X, X \backslash A; G) \rightarrow H_X^{n-q}(A; G)$$

is an isomorphism for every integer q and every Abelian group G.

Proof. Let V be a coordinate neighborhood of X which contains A. Then we obtain an isomorphism

$$e_*: H_q(V, V \backslash A; G) \approx H_q(X, X \backslash A; G)$$

induced by the inclusion map $e: (V, V \backslash A) \rightarrow (X, X \backslash A)$.

The inclusion map $f: [V^2, V \backslash d(V)] \rightarrow [X^2, X^2 \backslash d(X)]$ induces a homomorphism

$$f^*: H^n[X^2, X^2 \backslash d(X)] \rightarrow H^n[V^2, V^2 \backslash d(V)].$$

Then the element

$$v = f^*(u) \in H^n[V^2, V^2 \backslash d(V)]$$

is an orientation of the n-manifold V. Since V is homeomorphic to R^n, it follows from (5.1) that

$$\beta_v: H_q(V, V \backslash A; G) \rightarrow H_V^{n-q}(A; G)$$

is an isomorphism for every integer q and every Abelian group G.

Since V is a neighborhood of A in X, the system $\mathcal{M}$ of all neighborhoods of A in V is a cofinal subset of the system $\mathcal{N}$ of all neighborhoods of A

in X. Hence the inclusion $\mathcal{M} \subset \mathcal{N}$ induces an isomorphism

$$i^*: H_V^{n-q}(A; G) \approx H_X^{n-q}(A; G).$$

It is not difficult to verify that

$$\beta_u \circ e_* = i^* \circ \beta_v.$$

Consequently,

$$\beta_u = i^* \circ \beta_v \circ e_*^{-1}$$

is an isomorphism. This completes the proof of (5.2).   ‖

Theorem 5.3. *For every orientation u of an orientable n-manifold X and every compact subspace A of X, the homomorphism*

$$\beta_u: H_q(X, X \backslash A; G) \to H_X^{n-q}(A; G)$$

is an isomorphism for every integer q and every Abelian group G.

Proof. To establish (5.3) by induction, let $k \geq 1$ and assume that (5.3) has been proved for every compact subspace A of X which can be covered by not more than k coordinate neighborhoods of X. Because of (5.2), our inductive hypothesis is true when $k = 1$.

Now let A denote any compact subspace of X which can be covered by $k + 1$ coordinate neighborhoods of X, say, $V_0, V_1, \ldots, V_k$. Let

$$B = A \backslash V_0,$$
$$C = A \backslash (V_1 \cup \cdots \cup V_k).$$

Then B and C are compact subspaces of X satisfying

$$B \subset V_1 \cup \cdots \cup V_k, \quad C \subset V_0.$$

According to our inductive hypothesis, we have

$$\beta_u: H_q(X, X \backslash B; G) \approx H_X^{n-q}(B; G),$$
$$\beta_u: H_q(X, X \backslash C; G) \approx H_X^{n-q}(C; G).$$

For every integer q, let

$$E_q = H_q(X, X \backslash B; G) \oplus H_q(X, X \backslash C; G),$$
$$F^{n-q} = H_X^{n-q}(B; G) \otimes H_X^{n-q}(C; G).$$

Then we have an isomorphism

$$\alpha_q = \beta_u \otimes \beta_u: E_q \approx F^{n-q}.$$

Since A is covered by $V_0, V_1, \ldots, V_k$, we have

$$A = B \cup C.$$

On the other hand, let

$$D = B \cap C.$$

Then D is a compact subspace of X contained in the coordinate neighborhood V_0. According to (5.2), we have

$$\beta_u: H_q(X, X \backslash D; G) \approx H_X^{n-q}(D; G).$$

Now consider the following diagram:

$$\cdots \to E_{q+1} \xrightarrow{\phi} H_{q+1}(X, X \backslash D; G) \xrightarrow{\Delta} H_q(X, X \backslash A; G) \xrightarrow{\psi} E_q \to \cdots$$

$$\downarrow \alpha_{q+1} \qquad \downarrow \beta_u \qquad\qquad\qquad \downarrow \beta_u \qquad\qquad \downarrow \alpha_q$$

$$\cdots \to F^{n-q-1} \xrightarrow{\psi} H_X^{n-q-1}(D; G) \xrightarrow{\Delta} H_X^{n-q}(A; G) \xrightarrow{\phi} F^{n-q} \to \cdots$$

Here, the top row is the exact relative Mayer-Vietoris sequence for homology of the proper topological triad $(X; X \backslash B, X \backslash C)$ as given in [H5, p. 114], and the bottom row is the exact Mayer-Vietoris sequence in Exercise 3C.

By means of Exercise 2D, one can easily prove that the left rectangle and the right rectangle in the preceding diagram are both commutative. By means of Exercise 2E, one can also show that the central rectangle is commutative up to possibly a sign. Hence we may apply the five lemma [H2, p. 76] to the preceding diagram. Because of

$$\beta_u: H_q(X, X \backslash D; G) \approx H_X^{n-q}(D; G),$$

$$\alpha_q: E_q \approx F^{n-q}$$

for every integer q, it follows from the five lemma that the homomorphism

$$\beta_u: H_q(X, X \backslash A; G) \to H_X^{n-q}(A; G)$$

is an isomorphism for every integer q. This completes the induction and proves (5.3). $\parallel$

If the given n-manifold X is compact, then we may take A to be X itself. In this case, we have

$$H_X^{n-q}(X; G) = H^{n-q}(X; G)$$

in accordance with the definition in Sec. 3. Hence we obtain the following corollary of (5.3).

Corollary 5.4 (*Poincaré Duality Theorem*). *If X is a compact orientable n-manifold, then we have*

$$H_q(X; G) \approx H^{n-q}(X; G)$$

for every integer q and every Abelian group G.

In the preceding Poincaré duality theorem, we used both singular homology and singular cohomology. However, since X is an n-dimensional compact ANR according to [H4, p. 168, (7.1)], it follows from [H4, p. 141, (7.3)] that all homology (cohomology) theories coincide on X.

The remainder of the present section is devoted to the consequences of (5.4).

Corollary 5.5. *If X is a compact orientable n-manifold, then we have*

$$H_q(X; G) = 0, \qquad H^q(X; G) = 0$$

for every integer $q > n$ and every Abelian group G.

Proof. If $q > n$, then we have $n - q < 0$. Hence we obtain

$$H_q(X; G) \approx H^{n-q}(X; G) = 0,$$

$$H^q(X; G) \approx H_{n-q}(X; G) = 0.$$

This proves (5.5). ‖

Corollary 5.6. *If X is a connected compact orientable n-manifold, then we have*

$$H_n(X; G) \approx G, \qquad H^n(X; G) \approx G.$$

Proof. Since X is connected and locally pathwise connected, it follows that X is also pathwise connected. This implies that

$$H_0(X; G) \approx G, \qquad H^0(X; G) \approx G.$$

Hence we obtain

$$H_n(X; G) \approx H^0(X; G) \approx G,$$

$$H^n(X; G) \approx H_0(X; G) \approx G.$$

This completes the proof of (5.6). ‖

According to [H4, p. 141, (7.2)], the integral homology groups $H_q(X)$ and the integral cohomology groups $H^q(X)$ of a finite-dimensional compact ANR space X are finitely generated. Hence the Betti numbers, torsion coefficients, etc., of X are well defined. However, for the convenience of the proofs we shall assume throughout the remainder of the present section that X is a compact orientable n-manifold which has the same homotopy type as a finite cellular polytope; therefore, we may apply the results obtained in Sec. 5, Chap. 1.

Proposition 5.7. *For every integer q, the q-dimensional Betti number of X is equal to the $(n-q)$-dimensional Betti number of X.*

Proof. By definition, the q-dimensional Betti number of X is the rank of the Abelian group $H_q(X)$. Because of (5.4), we have

$$H_q(X) \approx H^{n-q}(X).$$

According to (5.6), Chap. 1, the rank of $H^{n-q}(X)$ is equal to the $(n-q)$-dimensional Betti number of X. This implies (5.7). ‖

Corollary 5.8. *If n is odd, then the Euler-Poincare characteristic $\chi(X)$ of X is zero.*

Proof. Let $n = 2k + 1$. If $\beta_q(X)$ denotes the q-dimensional Betti number of X, then we have

$$\chi(X) = \sum_{q=0}^{n} (-1)^q \beta_q(X) = \sum_{q=0}^{k} [(-1)^q + (-1)^{n-q}] \beta_q(X).$$

Since n is odd, we have

$$(-1)^q + (-1)^{n-q} = (-1)^q [1 + (-1)^n] = 0$$

for every integer q. This implies $\chi(X) = 0$. ‖

Proposition 5.9. *For every integer q, the q-dimensional torsion coefficients of X are the same as the $(n-q-1)$-dimensional torsion coefficients of X.*

Proof. By definition, the q-dimensional torsion coefficients of X is the torsion coefficients of the Abelian group $H_q(X)$. Because of (5.4), we have

$$H_q(X) \approx H^{n-q}(X).$$

According to (5.7), Chap. 1, the torsion coefficients of $H^{n-q}(X)$ are the same as the $(n-q-1)$-dimensional torsion coefficients of X. This implies (5.9). ‖

Corollary 5.10. *X is torsion-free in the dimensions* 0, $n - 1$, *and n.*
Proof. Since $H_{-1}(X) = 0$ and $H_0(X)$ is a free Abelian group according to [H5, p. 214, (3.2)], (5.10) is a direct consequence of (5.9). ‖

EXERCISES

5A. Generalize the homomorphism β_u in the text to a homomorphism

$$\beta_u \colon H_q(X \setminus B, X \setminus A; G) \to H_X^{n-q}(A, B; G)$$

for any compact pair (A, B) in X. Prove that this generalized β_u is an isomorphism for every integer q and every Abelian group G.

5B. By a *relative n-manifold*, we mean a topological pair (X, A) such that X is a Hausdorff space, A is a closed subspace of X, and $X \setminus A$ is an n-manifold. Prove the following *Lefschetz duality theorem for relative manifolds*: If (X, A) is a relative n-manifold, then we have

$$H_q(X \setminus A; G) \approx H_X^{n-q}(X, A; G)$$

for every integer q and every Abelian group G.

5C. By an *n-manifold with boundary*, we mean a relative n-manifold (X, A) such that X is paracompact and every point $x \in A$ has a neighborhood V in X with the property that the pair $(V, V \cap A)$ is homeomorphic to the pair $(R^{n-1} \times I, R^{n-1} \times 0)$. The subspace A of X is called the *boundary*. Since A may be empty, this definition contains the definition of n-manifolds as a special case. (X, A) is said to be *orientable* iff the n-manifold $X \setminus A$ is orientable. (X, A) is said to be *compact* iff X is compact. Establish the following *Lefschetz duality theorem for manifolds with boundary*: If (X, A) is a compact orientable n-manifold with boundary, then we have

$$H_q(X; G) \approx H_q(X \setminus A; G) \approx H^{n-q}(X, A; G),$$

$$H^q(X; G) \approx H^q(X \setminus A; G) \approx H_{n-q}(X, A; G)$$

for every integer q and every Abelian group G [Sp. p. 298].

BIBLIOGRAPHY

[A]   Alexandroff, P. S.: *Combinatorial Topology*. Vols. I–III. Gray-lock Press, Rochester, N.Y., 1956–1960.

[A-B]   Artin, E., and Braun, H.: *Vorlesungen über Algebraische Topologie*. Hamburg, 1964.

[A-H]   Alexandroff, P., and Hopf, H.: *Topologie*. Vol. I. Springer-Verlag, Berlin, Vienna, 1935.

[B]   Bourgin, D. G.: *Modern Algebraic Topology*. The Macmillan Company, New York, 1963.

[E-S]   Eilenberg, S., and Steenrod, N. E.: *Foundations of Algebraic Topology*. Princeton University Press, Princeton, N.J., 1952.

[G]   Godement, R: *Topologie Algébrique et Théorie des Faisceaux* (Actes sci. ind. 1252), Hermann & Cie, Paris, 1958.

[Gr]   Greenberg, M.: *Lectures on Algebraic Topology*. W. A. Benjamin, Inc., New York, 1966.

[H1]   Hu, S.-T.: *Elements of General Topology*. Holden-Day, Inc., San Francisco, 1964.

[H2]   Hu, S.-T.: *Elements of Modern Algebra*. Holden-Day, Inc., San Francisco, 1965.

[H3]   Hu, S.-T.: *Homotopy Theory*. Academic Press, Inc., New York, 1959.

[H4]   Hu, S.-T.: *Theory of Retracts*. Wayne State University Press, Detroit, 1965.

[H5]   Hu, S.-T.: *Homology Theory*. Holden-Day, Inc., San Francisco, 1966.

[H6]   Hu, S.-T.: *Introduction to Homological Algebra*. Holden-Day, Inc., San Francisco, 1968.

[H7]   Hu, S.-T.: *Introduction to General Topology*. Holden-Day, Inc., San Francisco, 1966.

[H-W] Hilton, P. J., and Wylie, S.: *Homology Theory, An Introduction to Algebraic Topology.* Cambridge University Press, New York, 1960.

[L] Lefschetz, S.: *Algebraic Topology.* Am. Math. Soc. Collective Publ., Vol. 27, 1942.

[M] Massey, W. S.: *Algebraic Topology, An Introduction.* Harcourt, Brace & World, Inc., New York, 1967.

[S] Schubert, H.: *Topologie.* B. G. Teubner Verlagsgesellschaft, m.b.H., Stuttgart, 1964.

[S-T] Seifert, H., and Threlfall, W.: *Lehrbuch der Topologie.* B. G. Teubner Verlagsgesellschaft, m.b.H., Stuttgart, 1934.

[Sp] Spanier, E. H.: *Algebraic Topology.* McGraw-Hill Book Co., Inc., New York, 1967.

[St] Steenrod, N. E.: *The Topology of Fibre Bundles.* Princeton University Press, Princeton, N.J., 1951.

[St-E] Steenrod, N. E., and Epstein, D. B. A.: *Cohomology Operations.* Princeton University Press, Princeton, N.J., 1962.

[Wa] Wallace, A. H.: *An Introduction to Algebraic Topology.* Pergamon Press, New York, 1957.

[Wh] Whitehead, G. W.: *Homotopy Theory.* The M.I.T. Press, Cambridge, Mass., 1966.

[Wi] Wilder, R. L.: *Topology of Manifolds.* Am. Math. Soc. Collective Publ., Vol. 32, 1949.

INDEX